50 Five-Minute Stories

50 Five-Minute Stories

Lynda Neilands

Eastbourne

ISBN – 10: 1 84291 277 1
ISBN – 13: 978 1 842912 77 5

Designed by pinnaclecreative.co.uk

Published by
Kingsway Communications Ltd
Lottbridge Drove, Eastbourne BN23 6NT, England.
Email: childrensministry@kingsway.co.uk

Printed in the USA

For David

CONTENTS

PART 3: AROUND THE WORLD

PART 4: INTO GOD'S WORD

ACKNOWLEDGEMENTS

I am indebted to many people for their help in preparing this book.

Particular thanks are due to Suzi Viana, Dr John Chaplin, Norman Cuthbert, Hetty and Alan Dorman, Laurence Graham, Dr Gerald Hall, the Revd John Hanna, Julie Heath, Alan and Margaret McElhinney, Andy Matheson, John Nonhebel, Demë Mustafaj, Andy Mathieson, Rosemary Scott, Brenda Thompson and Elizabeth Dunn Wilson for the material which they supplied for the stories from around the world.

I also wish to thank the Revd Dudley Levistone Cooney and the staff in the Humanities Department of Belfast Central Library for advice and practical help in relation to the historical section of the book.

Original versions of *'Lewis the Leaf'*, *'Snowdrop's First Christmas'* and *'The Seagull and the Shell'* were first published in *Together* magazine (National Society) in the Sept '85, Nov/Dec '85 and July/Aug '88 editions and are used with permission.

A final word of thanks must go to my family: to David for his unfailing support and to Christopher and Patrick for their boundless enthusiasm for stories. All three have encouraged me more than I can say.

50 Five-Minute Stories

INTRODUCTION

Stories work. The secular world knows it. Today's story-tellers may not be revered as they were in ancient times, but in the battle for employment, interviewees who answer questions with anecdotes greatly enhance their chances of landing the job.

Stories work. God confirms it. He's given us a Bible packed full of them. 'Jesus was not a theologian,' writes Madeleine L'Engle. 'He was God who told stories.'

You can see a story working when you look at the faces of the listeners. You can hear it in the quality of their silence. Good stories command attention. Moreover, they communicate values and ideas in a palatable, non-threatening way – putting flesh on the bare bones of concepts, teaching about life and lingering in the memory.

So how come children in church services and children's clubs so often get a homily or an object lesson, not a story?

One reason may be that teachers and preachers feel more comfortable with object lessons. A more probable explanation is that these hard-pressed leaders haven't been able to come up with the right story for that particular slot.

FINDING THAT STORY

The problem with many excellent stories is that they have not been written to be told aloud. They are too complex. Too wordy. This means that the hard-pressed minister, teacher or children's worker must adapt them to fit into a five- to ten-minute space. Another problem is that stories are not just required to fit in time-wise, they must often fit in with a chosen theme – 'Bible Sunday' … 'The Environment' … 'God's Sovereignty'. Last week you may have come across a great story on the theme of forgiveness, but the Brownies have requested something on 'caring for God's world'!

This book is designed to help would-be story-tellers. It contains fifty stories, written for *anyone* who wants to use stories to convey Christian values and biblical truth. Each story has been timed, and is accompanied by a suggested teaching point, an appropriate Bible reading and list of songs. In some cases additional information about characters and ideas for telling the story to a group are also included. Bible and subject indexes at the back point speakers to the material that fits their theme.

DIP IN OR WADE THROUGH

The stories may also be read through systematically. They are arranged in four sections: parable stories (to feed the imagination), historical stories (showing God as Master of time and history), stories from around the world (underlining the world-wide nature of the body of Christ) and Bible stories (a whistle-stop tour of the Old and New Testaments).

The book has been written primarily with the needs of those involved in leading church-based activities in mind, ie, ministers, leaders of all-age worship, Sunday school teachers, children's workers and leaders of uniformed organisations. But teachers may find it a useful source of stories for school assembly. And parents will find stories which provide a natural lead-in to bedtime prayers.

STAND AND DELIVER

Of course the real test of any story comes when you 'stand and deliver'. May I share a story from my own experience here – one illustrating the point that you don't have to feel you're a natural story-teller to tell successful stories?

Picture, if you will, a harassed mother sitting with her husband on their first Sunday in a new church, struggling to keep two-year-old twins under control. Suddenly the minister takes it upon himself to introduce them to the congregation.

'David is the incoming secretary of the Department of Youth and Children's work,' he explains. 'And his wife ... .' He hesitates, clearly desiring to bestow a separate identity on the dishevelled female before him as she fishes a two-year-old out from under her skirt. 'His wife is very good at telling children's stories.'

What! The woman almost falls out of the pew in shock. Whatever could have given the man that idea? She regularly uses stories to divert the two-man demolition squad from their destructive pursuits. But she certainly isn't in the habit of standing up in public and holding forth.

Still, the damage is done. Saddled with this unfounded reputation, she finds her imputed skills are in demand. The children in the Christian Endeavour are about to have their parents' evening. Please will she come and tell a story.

She goes in fear and trembling. Her mouth is dry. Her visual aids shake... .

And the story *still* works!

So if you're suffering from a similar lack of experience, be of good cheer! Some are born story-tellers. Others have story-telling thrust upon them. But take it from me – all you need to maintain the appearance of an expert story-teller is a suitable story told in accordance with a few ground rules.

TIPS ON STORY-TELLING

The ground rules for success in story-telling are as follows:

Eye contact

No matter what you say, it's going to be twice as effective if you look at the people you're speaking to. Story-telling is a shared experience. Where possible, speak to children directly. This could mean learning a story by heart. If a text is used, aim to know it sufficiently well to look up at significant points.

Expression

A flat, monotonous delivery drains life from the best material. Aim to know your story well enough to maximise its emotional appeal, working out in advance where excitement could be heightened through a change of pace or where suspense could be created by dropping your voice to a whisper.

Dialogue

To be vivid and convincing, characters need to speak for themselves. Reported speech *tells* the listeners what is going on. Direct speech *shows* them. Where possible, use different voices/accents for different characters.

Practice

Story-telling skills improve with practice. In her book *Creative Teaching Methods* (David C. Cook, 1985) Marlene LeFever recommends recording your voice as you read or tell a story and then listening to yourself the following day to assess where you can improve on your delivery. If you balk at a tape recorder practise in front of a mirror … or on the dog (ours is a first-class listener – just as long as I don't inadvertently use the word 'walk').

Illustrations

We've noted the importance of dialogue, but visual aids are important too. Today's children (and adults) expect to see as well as hear. The good news is you don't have to be artistic. Your visual aids could take the form of household objects mentioned in the story. And when it comes to drawings, colour matters more than draughtsmanship, and stick figures are fine! In fact a lack of artistic flair may even be an advantage…

Interaction

'What's this?' I ask, holding up my lop-sided donkey. If they're a co-operative little group, they'll tell me it's a donkey and pat themselves on the back for getting the right answer. 'A monster!' the less docile will yell gleefully. Either way a rapport is established! Interaction breaks down barriers and helps the listeners become involved in the story. With a mixed age-group, strategic questions to older children can aid younger children's comprehension. Think through your material in advance to assess where such questions may be asked or where your audience can help with sound effects (see below).

Sound effects

Check the story for sounds which may be simulated: bangs, crashes, hoof-beats, police-sirens, telephones, footsteps. Either reproduce them yourself or prepare the children beforehand to participate by making sounds or repeating phrases as required.

You will find a number of stories with specific instructions for interaction and sound effects in the Bible story section of this book.

Mime

If sufficient people are available and there is a suitable performing space, one person can read the story while the others mime the action. This saves the story-teller the bother of learning the story and making illustrations. But resist the temptation to produce it unrehearsed!

Explanation

One thing you may usefully point out is whether your story is true or made up. True stories tend to carry more weight than made-up stories (this is not to imply they are more valuable). Unless otherwise stated the stories in the historical, round-the-world, and Bible sections of this book are all substantially true, ie, they actually happened. After telling a parable-type story I sometimes say, 'This is not a true story, but there is truth in it... .' The children then help articulate that truth.

And finally ...

Don't let the fact that you won't have long enough to drive home the meaning prevent you from using a story. Stories often require less reinforcement than we may imagine to make their point. A few sentences or questions, followed by an appropriate song, should be enough.

'The highest moral and spiritual achievements depend not upon a push but a pull,' writes Reinhold Niebuhr.

I like to think that in some small ways these stories, springing from God's word and from the lives of his people, may exert that kind of pulling power.

Each story includes a note of the time the story takes to tell, the main teaching point, a relevant Bible passage and some suggested songs. These are taken from *Junior Praise* (JP), published by Marshall Pickering, *250 Songs For Children's Praise & Worship* (CPW), published by Children's Ministry and *Kidsource* (K), published by Kevin Mayhew.

PART ONE

THROUGH THE YEAR

50 Five-Minute Stories

The Knights Who Went to the Coast

LENGTH: 8 minutes. This story works well as a mime.

TEACHING POINT: God blesses those who are willing to change.

BIBLE READING: Matthew 19:16–22, 27–30

Once upon a time there were two knights. Sir Cuthbert was a tall brave knight and Sir Cedric was a small brave knight. Their job was to keep their land free from dragons and goblins and witches and enemies and evil-doers-of-every-description. In order to do this they carried big, shiny shields and wore lots of heavy armour.

Now keeping a land, even a small one, free of dragons and goblins and witches and enemies and evil-doers-of-every-description fifty-two weeks of the year is hard work. The two knights used to stagger in from the battlefield every evening totally worn out, until one day the queen took the king to one side.

'You know what, my darling,' she whispered in his ear. 'I think Sir Cuthbert and Sir Cedric are overdoing it.'

'Really?' said the king.

'Yes. And you know what, my angel? I think they need a break.'

'A break?' said the king.

'Yes, my beloved one. I think you should send them off on holiday.'

So the king sent for Sir Cuthbert and Sir Cedric.

'We've decided to send you boys to the coast for a week,' the queen explained. 'I want you to make sandcastles and paddle and fish and play ball. You'll come back new men.'

Well, even though Sir Cuthbert and Sir Cedric had never been to the coast before they were too tired to get excited. Still, they staggered off to the village store and bought all the things the queen said they would need: two sets of swimming trunks, two towels, two fishing rods, not forgetting of course two buckets and spades. They packed the whole lot into their saddle bags.

'We're off to the coast on Friday,' they wearily told all their friends and relations.

And their friends and relations were delighted to hear the news. 'That's great! It'll do you the world of good,' they all said.

At last Friday came and the king and queen were there to see the knights off. Sir Cuthbert climbed wearily onto his big black horse and Sir Cedric climbed wearily onto his small brown horse. Everyone waved and cheered, and away they went.

For a while they plodded along in silence, side by side. Then Sir Cedric turned to his friend with a weary frown and said, 'Cuthbert, do you really think this holiday will do the trick?'

'How do you mean – do the trick?'

'I mean, will a week at the coast really turn us into new men? The queen is expecting us to come back with loads of energy. I hope she's right.'

'So do I,' Sir Cuthbert sighed.

A couple of hours later they rode round a bend in the road – and there before them was a wonderful sight: sparkling blue sea, shimmering white sand, shady green palm trees.

'That must be the beach,' said Sir Cuthbert. 'I suppose we'd better build a couple of sandcastles before lunch.'

For the next three days the knights did everything the queen had told them to do. When the sun came up they kicked the beach-ball about and then they built a few sandcastles and then they kicked the beach-ball about some more. And when the sun went down they wrote postcards telling all their friends and relatives how hard they were trying to enjoy themselves.

'How long have we been here?' Sir Cedric asked Sir Cuthbert after breakfast on the fourth day.

Sir Cuthbert did some calculations. 'Three days, ten hours, forty minutes and twenty-five seconds to be precise. Are you beginning to feel like a new man yet?'

More wearily than ever, Sir Cedric shook his head. 'I feel even worse than I felt when we arrived here three days ago.'

'Me too,' Sir Cuthbert sighed.

Oh dear! The last thing they wanted to do was admit that the queen might be wrong and the holiday wasn't doing the trick.

Gloomily Sir Cuthbert looked at the sea. 'Maybe we haven't done enough swimming.'

'The last time we tried swimming I nearly drowned,' Sir Cedric pointed out.

'Well maybe we need to build a few more sandcastles.'

'If I have to fill my bucket with sand one more time, I think I'll collapse,' said Sir Cedric.

'OK then. Maybe we just need to put on some more sun-block and crash out on our mats.'

'Cuthbert,' said Sir Cedric firmly. 'I refuse to smear any more of that greasy stuff over my armour. My helmet is already so slippery, I keep dropping it. It took me ages getting it on this morning.'

'Yeah. I know what you mean,' Sir Cuthbert agreed gloomily. 'It took me ages getting into my armour too.'

Sadly the knights looked at each other. And then, from somewhere, a really daring thought popped up in Sir Cedric's mind.

'Cuthbert,' he said. 'Do you think the holiday might work better if we took off our armour? I mean … if we weren't wearing armour, running around wouldn't take such an effort. We could feel the sun on our backs and the sand beneath our toes. We'd be cooler and more comfortable. We might even be able to swim without sinking. . . .'

'But we're knights!' gasped Sir Cuthbert. 'No one ever sees knights without armour. We have to defend ourselves against dragons and goblins and witches and enemies and evil-doers-of-every-description. They might attack us...or worse...they might laugh at our knobbly knees.'

But Sir Cedric wasn't listening. He had disappeared behind a rock. And when he came out again Sir Cuthbert could hardly believe his eyes. His friend was wearing nothing but a pair of striped bathing trunks.

'Cedric!' he gasped. 'You're mad.'

'Maybe I am,' said Sir Cedric. 'But I don't care. I'm not weighed down any more. I feel like a new man. . . .' And away he went, racing across the sand, jumping and whooping with delight. Next thing he was splashing around in the sea.

'Come and join me,' he called to his friend, who was still sitting sweating it out on the beach under twenty-five kilos of chain-mail. 'Take off your armour. You can't imagine the difference it makes.'

But Sir Cuthbert wouldn't. He couldn't bear the thought of anyone – not even his best friend – seeing him without armour. And at the end of the week he went back to his battles more weary and worn out than ever, while Sir Cedric went home healthy as a herb bed and happy as a jester – totally refreshed by the sun and the sea and the sand.

SUGGESTED SONGS:

Big man standing by the blue waterside (JP 16) (K 422)

Come let us sing of a wonderful love (JP 29)

If you want joy, real joy, wonderful joy (JP 96) (CPW 110)

Jesus is knocking, patiently waiting (JP 135)

O happy day that fixed my choice (JP 178)

Spirit of the living God, fall afresh on me (JP 222)

There's new life in Jesus, Lift up your heart (JP 249)

Get up out of bed (JP 343)

Flower Power

LENGTH: 3–4 minutes

TEACHING POINT: Being right with God isn't about keeping rules, it's about confessing our sins and asking for forgiveness.

BIBLE READING: Luke 18:9–14

Once upon a time a dandelion seed landed beside a brook on the edge of a forest. It put down roots. Before long it had grown up straight and strong – and produced a handsome blossom.

When the dandelion looked into the brook and saw its fine appearance, it said to itself, 'The lion is king of the jungle, and the sun is king of the sky. I shall be king of the forest.'

'Tell the flowers they've just got themselves a new ruler,' it ordered a passing bee.

'Ze dandelion izzz king. Ze dandelion izzz king,' the bee went buzzing through the forest.

'Has the dandelion any right to be king?' wondered the bluebell.

'I don't know,' said the daisy. 'Let's ask the wise owl.'

The wise owl consulted her book of forest law. 'The law says that it takes a greater king to make a lesser king,' she informed them. 'The dandelion needs the sun's blessing to reign.'

When the dandelion heard this, it arranged to meet the sun first thing the following morning.

Then it called the flowers together. 'In future I'll expect to see some improvements in forest life,' it announced.

The first improvement was to do with their behaviour: 'From now on all flowers must open punctually at the crack of dawn,' the dandelion said.

The second improvement was to do with the way they looked. 'There's far too much variety around here,' the dandelion grumbled. 'From now on flowers can only wear round golden blossoms – like mine.'

The third improvement was to do with thorns. While speaking of thorns, the dandelion dropped its voice and sounded very religious. 'Thorns are bad and flowers shouldn't have them,' it warned. 'Only thorn-free flowers will get to heaven.'

When the wild rose rambling through the brambles on the other side of the brook heard this it pretended not to care. 'That's that then. I've more thorns than petals. No heaven for me!' it said.

Next morning, at dawn, the sun appeared. His white light sparkled on the water. The colours of his train splashed across the sky.

Proudly the dandelion stood before him. 'Oh Sun, I thank you that I am not like other flowers – noisy bluebells, droopy snowdrops, creeping violets. I especially thank you that I'm not all thorny like that dreadful rose over there. I'm round – like you. And golden – like you. And my stem's as smooth as silk.'

It sat back then and waited for the sun's blessing.

For a moment there was silence. Then, suddenly, the wild rose raised its voice. It hadn't meant to say anything ... but the sunlight was so pure ... and it felt so thorny. 'Have mercy! Have mercy on me, oh Sun,' it cried. 'I'm sorry about my thorns.'

Immediately the sun blessed the rose. He blessed it until its petals opened wide and its scent filled the forest.

'No! No! You've blessed the wrong flower.' Angrily the dandelion tossed its head. Hmm – that was funny! Its petals felt lighter than usual. It turned to check its appearance in the brook and gasped with dismay. Oh no! There, in place of its golden head, was a pathetic ball of fluff.

'My crown! My crown has gone!' it cried.

'It zeems you aren't king after all,' buzzed the bee.

SUGGESTED SONGS:

Amazing grace! (JP 8) (K 9)

Hark, the glad sound! the Saviour comes (JP 68)

I have seen the golden sunshine (JP 99)

I was lost but Jesus found me (JP 125)

Tell out, my soul, the greatness of the Lord (JP 229)

Lord we ask now to receive Your blessing (JP 301)

All you have to do is to ask the Lord (JP 307)

God of all mercy (JP 350)

Sometimes I'm naughty (JP 460)

Slasher, Basher and Wallop

LENGTH: 5–6 minutes

TEACHING POINT: God gives us help in the present and hope for the future.

BIBLE READING: Hebrews 4:14–16; Psalm 121

Wallop was a tennis ball. He lived in a broom cupboard under the stairs with two rackets, an umbrella and a walking-stick. He was happy in the broom cupboard, but he hated the days when he was taken off to the tennis court to be slammed to and fro across a net.

Biff! – 'Ouch!' Thwack! – 'Owww!'

It hurt. It really did.

'How I wish the summer was over,' he moaned one evening. 'I used to be white and fluffy. And now look! I'm all worn and covered in grey bruises.'

He might have known he'd get no sympathy from the tennis rackets. They were called Slasher and Basher, and all they cared about was winning matches.

'You won't even last to the end of the summer,' Slasher said nastily. 'You're losing your bounce. My human will dump you.'

'He's right,' agreed Basher. 'A tennis ball that's lost its bounce is only good for the scrapheap.'

That night Wallop felt so miserable he couldn't sleep. 'Help me! Oh help me, help me,' he cried to no one in particular.

Now Wallop had never seen an angel. In fact, if you'd asked him beforehand, he'd have said he didn't believe in angels. But when a bright being suddenly appeared beside the walking-stick, Wallop knew without a shadow of doubt that an angel is what it was.

'Cheer up, Wallop,' the angel said. 'You asked for help. So I've brought it. Just hold still for a moment.'

Wallop felt a slight pressure on one of his bruises, followed by a lovely all-over warmth.

'There!' said the angel. 'You've got wings now.'

'Where?' said Wallop, rolling out in front of the mirror. 'I don't see any wings.'

'That's because they're invisible,' explained the angel. 'But the more you use them, the bigger and the stronger they'll grow. Which reminds me – I've got something else for you.'

'Will I be able to see it?' Wallop wondered.

'No!' laughed the angel. 'It's a new name.'

'So what am I to be called then?' asked Wallop, hoping it would be something with a ring to it, like Alphonsus or Sylvester.

The angel looked mischievous and mysterious at the same time. 'You'll find out when your wings are fully grown.' And with that it disappeared.

Wallop was full of excitement. 'Slasher! Basher! Wake up!' He couldn't wait to tell them what had happened. 'I've just met an angel. And guess what! It gave me invisible wings and a new name!'

The rackets burst out laughing.

'That last match has scrambled your brains, Wallop,' chuckled Slasher. 'You're ready for the scrapheap for sure.'

'No I'm not,' cried Wallop. 'Not now I've got wings.'

'You'll need them, mate,' Basher cackled. 'I heard my human say there's a tournament tomorrow.'

'A tournament?' Wallop's heart sank. A tournament meant he wouldn't just be knocked around for an hour or two. He would have to keep bouncing all day.

Sure enough, the humans took the ball and rackets out of the cupboard and brought them to the tennis court next morning.

'Here I come. Brace yourself!' Slasher sneered as Wallop was thrown up in the air for the first shot of the opening match.

'Help me ... help me . . .' Wallop whispered, not sure if he *really* had invisible wings, but doing his best to flap anyway.

'Hey! What happened there?' Slasher's human cried as the racket hit thin air.

What had actually happened was that Wallop had flapped two centimetres out of reach. But of course the humans didn't know that.

'It's as if our rackets are full of holes,' they complained when they were both put out in the first round.

'That's right – blame us!' hissed Slasher. 'It isn't our fault. It's the ball.'

Wallop gave a little bounce of delight. Invisible wings hadn't saved him from every knock, but they'd certainly made a difference.

'Thank you, Angel,' he whispered, hoping the angel, wherever it was, would hear.

Unfortunately it was Basher who heard. 'Save your breath,' he warned. 'You'll need it. Invisible wings might have got you through the first part of the tournament. But they're going to play doubles now. That means twice as many rackets, hitting you twice as often, twice as hard.'

Biff! – 'Ouch!' Thwack! – 'Owww!'

The racket was right. The second half was worse than the first. Much worse. Game after game Wallop was slammed around the court. The strokes hit him so fast he couldn't even think, never mind fly. He did his best, flapping as much as he could, but he kept losing concentration. Towards the end of the last set he thudded onto the ground and all he could manage was one feeble little bounce.

'Next stop the scrapheap,' hissed Slasher, swinging him a final mighty whack.

'Help me...help me....' Wallop hurtled up into the air.

'Well done. You've a great set of wings there!' a voice cheered.

It was the angel.

'But I've lost my bounce,' Wallop cried.

'Swallows don't need to bounce.'

What was that supposed to mean? Wallop looked over his shoulder and – goodness! – his wings weren't invisible any more. He could see them, smooth and grey, feathery, glistening in the sun. At the sight of those feathers everything became clear. It was amazing! A miracle!

'I'm a bird. My name is Swallow....' He swooped and soared.

While down on the tennis court four humans searched for the missing ball.

SUGGESTED SONGS:

Because He lives (JP 58)

Amazing grace! (JP 8) (K 9)

Be bold, Be strong (JP 14) (CPW 11) (K 17)

Father, hear the prayer we offer (JP 41)

Father, lead me day by day (JP 43)

We shall overcome (JP 270)

When the road is rough and steep (JP 279)

We need to grow, grow, grow, grow (JP 484) (K 359)

The Seagull and the Shell

LENGTH: 4 minutes

TEACHING POINT: God wants to fill our lives with his power.

BIBLE READING: Ephesians 1:15–23

The summer was over and the last of the holiday-makers had gone home. From his perch on the cliff-top a seagull flew onto the deserted beach and walked among the shells.

'See the sea! See the sea!' he called.

The shells ignored him. Now that the holiday season was over, there didn't seem much point in talking, and, in any case, they had nothing to say to a gull.

'See the sea! See the sea!' the seagull kept repeating – until a strange sobbing sound interrupted his calls.

'Boo hoo hoo. Boo hoo hoo.'

The gull peered around with bright searching eyes. Three hops from a hump-shaped rock he spotted its source.

'Boo hoo hoo. Boo hoo hoo.' A very ordinary grey-and-white shell, about the size of a fifty-pence piece, was sitting in a shallow circle of water, crying wetly.

'Why are you crying, Shell?' the seagull asked.

'Because…boo hoo…I'm unhappy.'

'Why? What's gone wrong?'

'Everything!' wailed the shell. 'No one wants me. I'm the wrong shape and the wrong size and the wrong colour. Boo hoo hoo hoo.'

The seagull nestled down in the sand. He knew that every shell longed to be picked up and taken home by a holiday-maker.

'You look all right to me, Shell,' he said.

'Do I?' Though the shell perked up slightly, the improvement didn't last. 'That's because … boo hoo … you're a gull … boo hoo. If you were human, you'd see how useless I am.'

'Useless?' The seagull cocked his sleek head to one side.

'Totally. Boo hoo. I'm too dull to stick on a jewellery box and too small to work as a soap dish.'

'That's good,' chirped the seagull. 'I'd hate to be glued in one place or have slimy soap sitting on my stomach.'

'But I'm not even curvy enough to decorate a coffee table and be picked up by visitors.'

'A lucky escape! Who wants to study the wax in human ears?'

'I do.' The shell was angry now. 'Anything would be better than sitting here day after day just waiting for something to happen. I can't think why I even talked to you in the first place. You're a gull. You don't understand.'

'I understand perfectly,' the seagull nodded. 'Like every other shell on this beach, you feel empty inside.'

Empty. The shell seemed to shrink into the sand, becoming smaller and duller than ever.

'Go away, Gull,' it muttered.

'You don't *have* to be empty, you know. Why not ask me to change things for you?'

'I'm asking you to GO AWAY.'

'Very well.' The seagull rose. 'Goodbye.'

'No! Wait! I didn't mean that. I don't want to be empty. Please stay and change things for me if you can.'

Three hops and the shell found itself lifted gently yet firmly in a bright yellow beak.

'Help! Stop it! Put me back!' it shrieked. 'No, not like that! Put me back properly.'

'I have,' said the seagull. 'I've turned your downside up.'

Sure enough, the hollow of the shell's mother-of-pearl underside was exposed to the sky. It wobbled, struggling to balance on the curve of its grey-and-white back.

'Just relax! There's nothing to worry about!' the seagull said reassuringly. Next minute the shell was somersaulting forward, caught up in the foaming swirl of an incoming wave.

'Wh-wh-what was that?' it gasped as the wave swirled out again.

'That was the sea washing over you.'

'But … but it was *wonderful!* I mean the sea has washed over me twice a day for as long as I can remember, and it never felt like *that!*'

'Your downside is up, Shell. Things are different now.'

A second wave swept in and up and over the shell and back.

'Oh Gull,' the shell cried. 'I can't think why I ever wanted to leave the beach. I don't feel the least bit empty any more.'

'Your downside is up now, Shell. You're full of sea.'

A third wave came, closely followed by a fourth and then a fifth.

By this time the shell was yards away from the rock, relaxing and enjoying itself more and more with every swirl. From the crest of the sixth wave it caught sight of the other shells stuck in their usual rows, all clinging to the sand.

'Poor things,' it murmured. 'Living downside down gets you nowhere. If only they knew how exciting it was to change.'

'So why not tell them?' suggested the seagull.

'Oh I couldn't, could I? I mean, what would I say?'

'Say you're on the same beach, but everything's different. And let them ask why.'

Woosh! A seventh wave, higher, fleecier and more powerful than the rest lifted the shell and carried it all the way back to the hump-shaped rock.

'All right,' it called. 'I will. And thank you, Gull.'

'You're welcome.'

The seagull spread its wings. Flapping and gliding he swooped across the beach. As the autumn sky darkened above the evening tide, his call echoed gladly.

'See the sea! See the sea! See the sea!'

SUGGESTED SONGS:

All over the world the Spirit is moving (JP 5) (CPW 5)

For I'm building a people of power (JP 47) (CPW 48) (K 61)

God whose Son was once a man on earth (JP 62)

Spirit of the living God, fall afresh on me (JP 222)

Wherever I am I will praise you, Lord (JP 283)

Wide, wide as the ocean (JP 292)

Hang on, stand still (JP 356) (CPW 77) (K 94)

Lewis the Leaf

LENGTH: 4 minutes. This story works well as a mime. Two people in addition to the narrator are required to play the parts of the wind and the tree. (Lewis is a large paper leaf with a happy face on one side and a sad face on the other.)

TEACHING POINT: God wants us to get to know him not just as our Creator but as our Friend.

BIBLE READING: Jeremiah 9:23–24

Once upon a time there was a leaf called Lewis. He was called Lewis because that was the way he felt – very, very loo-wis, as if he might drop off the tree any minute. All his friends had dropped off. They had been swept up by the gardener and burnt on a huge bonfire. Lewis was the very last leaf left on the tree, which meant he wasn't just feeling loose, he was feeling lonely too.

'Oh how I miss my friends,' he sighed. 'How I wish I had someone to talk to.'

He tried talking to the twigs. But it wasn't much use.

'Be quiet you silly Leaf,' they said. 'We're making plans for next spring. We're too busy to talk to you.'

So he tried talking to the branches. But that wasn't much use either.

'Don't interrupt, Lewis,' they said. 'We're deciding how many twigs we can support next year.'

He even tried talking to the old trunk.

'Have you any idea how hard I must work getting minerals out of the soil?' the trunk groaned. 'All I want in autumn is a bit of peace and quiet.'

Nobody had any time for Lewis.

Sadly he hung there with nothing to do and no one to talk to.

And then it happened – a breath, an unmistakable murmur: 'Why not talk to me?' said a voice.

It was the wind.

'But … but … I can't talk to *you!*' Lewis quivered from point to stem. 'A leaf can't talk to the mighty wind.'

'Why not?' said the wind.

'Because … well … because I'm not clever enough. I wouldn't know what to say.'

'Who says you aren't clever?' swooshed the wind. 'Listen to me, Lewis. You know more than you think.' And with these words the wind departed as unmistakably as it had appeared.

Even though the conversation had only lasted a few seconds, Lewis felt a lot more cheerful.

In fact he felt so cheerful he started to hum. 'I know more than I think, tee-tum. I know more than I think, tee-tum.'

'Be quiet you silly Leaf,' cried all the twigs and branches.

'I'm sorry, tee-tum. I can't help it, tee-tum. I'm happy!'

'Happiness is no excuse for noise,' said the old trunk sleepily. 'Especially when you've nothing to be happy about.'

'Oh but I have. I've just discovered something. I know more than I think.'

'You've discovered nothing of the sort,' snorted the old trunk. 'A twig knows something because it knows how to grow leaves. Can you grow leaves?'

'No,' said Lewis.

'A branch knows something because it knows how to support twigs. Can you support twigs?'

'No,' said Lewis.

'A trunk knows something because it knows how to draw minerals out of the soil. Can you draw minerals out of the soil?'

'No,' said Lewis.

'Well, there you are then!' pronounced the trunk. 'You see, Lewis, you're stupid. You know nothing at all.'

'Hear, hear!' cried the twigs and branches.

'But ... but the wind told me . . .' stammered Lewis.

At the mention of the wind's name the trunk lost its temper. 'How dare you! How dare you say such a thing! The wind is a mighty powerful force, feared and revered by countless trees in innumerable gardens all over the land. It shakes the earth and moves the heavens. But it does not speak. No. Not only do you know nothing, Leaf. Worse than that, you tell lies.'

'Foolish lying Leaf!' cried all the twigs and branches. 'You're nothing but a noisy nuisance. Why don't you drop off?'

All the happiness had drained out of Lewis's veins. He shrivelled, drooping on his stem.

'All right,' he said. 'I will.'

And he let go.

Swoosh. Next thing he knew he was being lifted and carried up, up into the air. It was like being at a funfair. First he went on the big wheel. Then he went on the helter-skelter. And then he went on the merry-go-round.

'Are you enjoying this?' called the wind.

'It's fantastic,' Lewis cried. 'But could we stop – just for a minute? There's something I wanted to ask you. ... '

'Go ahead. I'm listening.' The wind dropped.

'Well ... um. ... it's just that I'm a bit puzzled. I've always felt stupid. I mean, I can't grow leaves or support twigs or draw minerals from the soil. So I was just wondering – what do I know?'

'Come on, Lewis. Haven't you worked that out yet?' smiled the wind. 'I'll give you a clue. It's not what you know ... it's who you know. . . .'

'"It's not what you know … it's who you know." Hey, wait a minute … I know YOU!'

'Exactly.' With an almighty swoosh the wind lifted Lewis high up into the air, and away they whirled together.

SUGGESTED SONGS:

God who made the earth (JP 63)

Happiness is to know the Saviour (JP 70)

I'm special because God has loved me (JP 106) (CPW 115) (K 162)

I'm very glad of God (JP 107)

In the stars His handiwork I see (JP 112)

My Lord is higher than a mountain (JP 170)

The greatest thing in all my life is knowing you (JP 239)

There are hundreds of sparrows, thousands,
    millions (JP 246) (CPW 206) (K 320)

The wise may bring their learning (JP 253)

Whether you're one or whether you're two (JP 284) (K 384)

Snowdrop's First Christmas

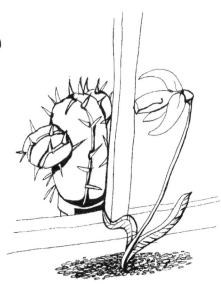

LENGTH: 4 minutes

TEACHING POINT: The meaning of Christmas.

BIBLE READING: Luke 2:1–20

On Christmas morning Snowdrop woke up hoping she'd got taller in the night. She held her breath as she raised her head. And yes, she'd made it. At long last she could see out of the windowbox into the lounge.

It was more beautiful than she'd ever imagined. There, in the corner, was the Christmas tree, decked with fairy lights and ribbons. Glasses gleamed upon the table. Strings of brightly coloured cards hung around the walls. And there were presents – so many presents – piled on the floor.

'So this is Christmas Day. Oh my!' Snowdrop marvelled. 'Isn't it exciting?'

'Not particularly.' On the other side of the pane Cactus sounded as prickly as he looked. 'When you've seen as many Christmases as I have … hmph … the novelty wears off. This year will be the same as last year and the year before. The room will be too hot and far too noisy. I'll end up sharing my sill with some silly, gaudy pot plant, forced to make polite conversation.'

'But don't you like to see the family enjoying themselves?' cried Snowdrop.

'Enjoying themselves! Whatever gave you that idea? The family don't enjoy Christmas any more than I do. They're worn out working in the shop. Right now Mrs Smith is in the kitchen wondering how she'll survive and Mr Smith is bracing himself with something strong they bought for the pudding.'

Snowdrop drooped a little. 'What a shame!' She brightened up again. 'At least the children will enjoy themselves. I mean, just look at all those presents.'

Cactus snorted. 'Last year Justin's remote control speed boat wouldn't work. Sarah wanted a pony but didn't get one. And baby Amy pulled the head off Natasha's doll. They ended up, as usual, squabbling and sulking.'

'Perhaps things will be different this year,' murmured Snowdrop.

'Fat chance. Look, they're coming in now. Just watch.'

Anxiously Snowdrop watched as Mr and Mrs Smith showed the relatives into the room. And yes, Mrs Smith did look exhausted. And yes, Mr Smith did appear to have had a drink or two. And oh dear, the relatives had brought a magnificent scarlet amaryllis in a pot.

'Here we go again!' Cactus bristled as it was set beside him on the sill.

It was all such a let-down Snowdrop didn't want to look any more. She drooped away from the window, heavy with disappointment.

Time passed. The glass steamed up. The daylight faded. The curtains were drawn.

'What's wrong, Snowdrop? You seem sad,' someone called.

Snowdrop lifted her head and saw a single star glimmering in the evening sky.

'I am sad,' she sighed. 'I've had a great disappointment. All week I've been looking forward to Christmas Day only to discover that nobody enjoys it.'

'Nobody enjoys Christmas Day! I've never heard such nonsense. Why, stars and angels have a wonderful time. We spend hours and hours before the gates of heaven, worshipping the Lord of the universe and remembering.'

'Remembering what?'

'The first Christmas. We remember how he came to live with people on earth. Snowdrop? I say, Snowdrop, you look pale. Are you all right?'

'I'm just shocked,' Snowdrop nodded. 'I'd no idea. About the Lord of the universe, I mean. Please tell me more.'

They talked all night. By morning Snowdrop was ready to burst with excitement. She couldn't wait to tell Cactus what Christmas was about.

At long last Mrs Smith pulled back the curtains.

'Oh Cactus, you'll never guess. . . .'

But her plant friend had news of his own. 'There was a power cut yesterday,' he informed her. 'Just after they closed the curtains. The lights went off. The TV went off. The family were in a fine state, I'm telling you.'

'Well I never! What did they do?'

'You won't believe this. When the panic died down they lit candles, sat together in semi-darkness and the kids put on a play about a baby being born in a stable. I don't know what got into them. I mean, we're talking here about a family of couch potatoes. But after the play Mr Smith accompanied Mrs Smith on the piano while she sang about shepherds and wise men and angels and stars. It was quite...' Cactus swallowed. 'Well, it was different anyway.'

'So they know after all!' exclaimed Snowdrop.

'Know what?'

'About the Lord of the universe coming to earth.'

'The Lord of the universe! Come here! I don't believe you!'

'It's true. He came as a baby.'

'When?'

'The first Christmas.'

'So what's *that* got to do with all *this*?' Cactus bristled in the direction of the tree, the tinsel and the cards.

'I'm not sure. The good thing is the family remembered the real meaning.'

'About time too,' Cactus snorted. But his prickles had calmed down.

'Happy Christmas, Cactus,' Snowdrop smiled.

SUGGESTED SONGS:

Infant holy, Infant lowly (JP 110) (K 554)

Mary had a little baby, Mary had a little baby (JP 164)

Born in the night (JP 313)

Christmas is a time, Christmas is a time (JP 321)

Christmas isn't Christmas till it happens in your heart (JP 322)

Come and join the celebration (JP 323) (CPW 25)

Crackers and turkeys and pudding and cream (JP 327) (K 35)

Girls and boys, leave your toys, make no noise (JP 344) (CPW 53)

Red Giant and White Dwarf

LENGTH: 4 minutes

TEACHING POINT: When God came into the world, ordinary people had a part to play. He has a special role for each of us in his kingdom today.

BIBLE READING: Matthew 1:18–25

Red Giant and White Dwarf met at the school for stars. They were in the same class – two unformed globules learning how to spin, how to produce heat, and most important, how to shine. Neither of them was brilliant, but they did their best, and after a few hundred light years, they passed all their exams. The time had come for them to go out into the universe, and that was when they made a big decision. They decided to work as a double act – shining and spinning together.

They found a position with a small constellation in the Milky Way Galaxy. It was a very minor role. But White Dwarf and Red Giant didn't mind. They settled down. Ages passed. And the two of them just got on with the routine business of twinkling.

So you could have knocked White Dwarf down with a meteor when one day she suddenly had a visit from the director. It didn't take the form of a big bang or a blinding light. It was a voice – quiet yet clear. 'White Dwarf,' the voice said, 'I want you to create an explosion.'

I beg your pardon! White Dwarf had learnt about explosions at school, but that was a long time ago and she'd never expected to make one. She hadn't a clue how to go about it.

'Red Giant will help you,' the voice went on.

Now White Dwarf had always believed the director knew best. So, even though she still had plenty of questions, she wasn't about to argue.

'All right then,' she said simply.

'Thank you – and White Dwarf . . .'

'Yes?'

'You're a very special star.'

A very special star? White Dwarf found that hard to believe. Special stars were stars like Sirius and Pollux who'd been given names by the people on earth. Still, it was nice to know the director valued her so highly.

She was thinking things over when Red Giant came back from his spin.

'How does a binary star like us create an explosion?' she asked.

'It's straightforward really. The dwarf star draws extra energy from the giant star so that its body temperature heats higher and higher until – POW! Everything blows.'

'I see,' said White Dwarf.

'Why do you want to know?'

She explained. Oh dear! As soon as Red Giant heard what the director wanted, he stopped being helpful and became angry. Very angry indeed.

'I'm amazed you'd even *consider* such a thing. Don't you realise how risky it is. Stars *die* in explosions. OK, you might survive. But it will blow us apart. We might never be together again.'

'You know I'd hate that,' cried White Dwarf. 'But. . . .'

'But what?'

'We can't say no to the director.'

'*I* can,' said Red Giant, and away he spun in a temper.

They'd never had such an argument. White Dwarf felt torn in two. 'The director knows best,' she was reminding herself with a rather wobbly twinkle when once again she heard his voice.

'What's the matter? Why are you flickering?'

'It's just … well … you see, Red Giant doesn't want to make an explosion. Couldn't you ask some other star?'

'You're the one I've chosen and set into place. Down on earth there are wise men watching the heavens for a sign. When you explode you'll shine a thousand times brighter than usual. They'll see you and they'll know it's time to act.'

'Men see *me!*' This was beyond White Dwarf's wildest dreams.

'You'll appear twice,' the director went on. 'Your first appearance will start them searching and your second appearance will show them where to look. Between appearances Red Giant will act like a curtain, hiding you from view.'

'That's the whole problem. He won't agree.' White Dwarf had started to flicker again.

'I think now that I've had a little chat with him, you'll find he sees things more clearly. Look, here he comes.'

Under other circumstances White Dwarf might have asked how the director could talk to her and to Red Giant at the same time. Right now she couldn't wait to find out whether Red Giant had really changed his mind.

'Well?' she said.

'Well yourself,' he twinkled back. And she could tell from his voice he wasn't angry any more.

'I know making an explosion is risky,' she said. 'But I'm sure the director has everything under control.'

'Listen, I was wrong. I didn't understand. He's the one taking the real risk. We're only exploding. The director's becoming a *baby* and going to *earth*.'

For a moment White Dwarf was silent … thunderstruck. The director. A *baby*! Why, babies were totally helpless. Who would look after him? Who would keep him safe? She'd heard stories about how cruel humans could be.

'A *baby*,' she gasped. 'But what if … ?'

'There are no what ifs. The director knows what he's doing. Remember that prophecy, the one we heard at school, about a child being born to a virgin?'

'Yes.'

'Well this is it.' Red Giant spun towards her. 'This is the greatest drama since creation – and we've got a star part.'

SUGGESTED SONGS:

As with gladness men of old (JP 9) (K 14)

Hark, the glad sound! the Saviour comes (JP 68)

In the stars His handiwork I see (JP 112)

Jesus Christ the Lord is born (JP 131)

The Virgin Mary had a baby boy (JP 251)

A special star is in the sky (JP 305)

Maybe you can't draw or sing or be a football star (JP 429)

This Child, secretly comes in the night (JP 480) (K 737)

The Tale of Scholar the Rabbit

LENGTH: 6–7 minutes

TEACHING POINT: Christians have a book which teaches them the truth.

BIBLE READING: 2 Timothy 3:14–17

It's a sad fact that some animals – like some humans – don't get along with their families. That's the way it was for Scholar the Rabbit. And truly, it wasn't his fault. He tried to be friends with his twin brothers, Robust and Reckless. But Robust was a big, strong, beefy rabbit and Reckless was a very brave and daring rabbit, and the two of them spent their time ganging up against Scholar and calling him horrible names.

The three rabbits lived in a burrow at the bottom of a lane. Scholar was a bit of a dreamer and liked nothing better than to lie in a ditch at the side of the lane and stare at the sky. The trouble was he hardly ever got peace to do this because of his brothers' bullying ways.

Anyway one day Scholar was hopping around in a bit of a day-dream just as usual when all of a sudden he noticed something very interesting lying in a ditch. As soon as he set eyes on it his heart leapt with joy and he couldn't wait to bring it back to the burrow.

It took a lot of effort, but finally he got there. Home at last! The only problem was that the twins were blocking the entrance.

'That's a funny-looking carrot,' Robust said.

'It isn't a carrot. It's a book. Please let me past,' Scholar squeaked.

'Here. Let's see what it tastes like.' Reckless started to nibble the edge of a page.

'No! No!' Scholar cried. 'You don't eat books. You open them and look at the pictures. Now let me through … please. … '

Robust nodded at Reckless. They moved to one side, smirking, while Scholar struggled into the burrow with his book.

By now he was really tired but very excited. He had never had a book of his own before. Holding his breath, he opened it up. He found himself looking at a picture of a bear. And as he stared something quite amazing happened. The little rabbit discovered he was able to understand the strange black squiggles underneath. They made sense. They told him something. 'Bears are very dangerous,' they said.

'Well I never!' Scholar whispered to himself. Eagerly he turned over to a picture of some chimpanzees. 'Chimpanzees are very intelligent,' the words told him.

Scholar's eyes widened. On the next page was a picture of an elephant. 'Elephants are the biggest animals of all,' he read, and suddenly he just couldn't keep his excitement to himself. 'Robust! Reckless! Something wonderful has happened,' he yelled. 'I know words. The book is speaking to me.'

It was the first time Scholar had ever known better than his brothers. They stood there, blinking with surprise, while he told them what the book said about bears and chimps and elephants. 'Aren't words brilliant?' Scholar's eyes shone. 'If you like I'll teach you what they say. Then you can read the book for yourselves.'

Robust and Reckless looked uneasy. 'Let's hear a bit more first.' Reckless turned over the pages until he came to a picture of a rat. 'Tell us what it says about rats.'

'Rats carry disease,' read Scholar proudly. 'Farmers often lay poison to get rid of them.'

'Hey, wait a minute!' Robust scowled. 'Some of my best friends are rats.'

'I'm sorry,' said Scholar. 'But that's what the book says.'

Robust's voice turned nasty. 'Well, let's hear what it has to say about rabbits then.'

Nervously Scholar began to read the page on rabbits. 'Rabbits are ... er. ... ' He stopped and swallowed.

'Are what? Go on,' hissed Robust.

'Must I?'

'Yes.'

'Rabbits are serious pests. ... '

'Serious pests!' Robust thumped his hind legs on the ground. 'Do you hear that, Reckless? This book is calling us names. So tell me, you Upside-down Daisy....' He thrust his nose up against his brother's and glared into his eyes. 'Do you believe the book? Do you think that it tells the truth?'

It was on the tip of Scholar's tongue to say no. But he was an honest rabbit. 'I ... I ... think the book knows more than I do,' he squeaked in the end.

That did it. 'Grab him!' Robust and Reckless seized their small brother by the ears. 'We're going for a little walk, Airhead,' Robust hissed as they hauled him out of the burrow into the lane. 'We're going up to the farmyard to visit the rats so you can tell them what it says in your book.'

'No! Let me go, you bullies!' Scholar struggled to escape. But the twins easily overpowered him. 'Help! Help!' he squeaked as they marched him down the lane towards the farmyard.

'He's hoping a bear or a chimp or an elephant will come and save him,' mocked Robust. 'How dumb can you get? There aren't any bears or chimps or elephants. They don't exist. The book is lies. And the sooner Goofy here understands that the better.' By this time they had reached the barn. Reckless held onto Scholar while Robust called through the open door. 'Out you come, Ratties. Our pea-brained brother has a book here which says some very nasty things about you.'

Twitching with fear, Scholar waited to hear the pattering of the rats' feet. What should he do? The rats were mean, vicious creatures. They wouldn't like being told they carried disease. Perhaps he should pretend the book was wrong. But even as the thought entered his head Scholar knew that if he wanted to remain an honest rabbit he couldn't do that. He loved the book and believed every word.

'Ratties,' Robust called again. 'Where are you?'

'We'd better find out,' he decided when the rats didn't appear.

Inside, the barn was dark and so silent Scholar could hear his heart beating.

'Sid! Gnasher! Whiptail!' Robust called his rat friends by name.

Still there was no answer and, as the rabbits' eyes became used to the dark of the barn, they suddenly saw why. The rats were there all right. They were there piled up in the middle of the floor. Eyes shut. Paws stiff.

'They're dead!' wailed Reckless.

'Oh! Oh!' Robust moaned. 'Poor Sid! Poor Gnasher! Poor old Whiptail!'

There was a moment of stunned silence. Then Reckless let go of Scholar's ears and Robust looked at his young brother with new respect.

'They've been poisoned,' he said. 'Poisoned by the farmer. Just like it says in Scholar's book.'

SUGGESTED SONGS:

Father, Your Word (JP 338) (K 58)

Have you got an appetite? (JP 357) (K 97)

I'm going to hide God's Word (JP 378)

I'm going to say my prayers (JP 379) (K 545)

If your empty tum is rumbling (JP 390)

Make the Book live to me, O Lord (JP 163)

The best book to read is the Bible (JP 234)

The Word of God (JP 474)

Maisie's Web

LENGTH: 5 minutes

TEACHING POINT: Whatever we do, we should do it for the Lord.

BIBLE READING: Colossians 3:23–24

Maisie the Spider lived in Professor Brown's house. She was a very ordinary spider, but she had one great gift. She could spin first-class webs. She spun her webs all over the house – in the kitchen, in the hallway, in the lounge. And as she spun she hoped and prayed. She wished and dreamt. And all her hopes and dreams and prayers and wishes were focused on one thing. Maisie wanted Professor Brown to admire what she did.

The trouble was the professor always had his nose in a book.

Then one day Maisie had an idea. She went into Professor Brown's study, climbed onto his desk and spun a mega-brilliant web on the anglepoise lamp. 'Now why didn't I think of that sooner?' she wondered as she scuttled back to admire her work. Surely even Professor Brown could not fail to see a work of art plonk in the middle of his desk.

She was more pleased than ever when she heard the sound of a key in the door. 'He's home early,' she thought. 'He'll come straight into the study.'

'Oh dearie, dearie me,' said a voice.

Maisie was startled. That wasn't the professor.

'The place hasn't seen a feather duster in years, I shouldn't wonder.'

Anxious to discover who had dared to come in when the professor was out, Maisie swung down from the desk and crept into the hallway.

There in the cloakroom stood a grey-haired woman with an apron and bucket. 'Dearie, dearie me! Just look at that.' The good news was she had noticed Maisie's creations. The bad news was she didn't like them. 'Cobwebs! Cobwebs everywhere,' she complained. Then, to the spider's horror, she rolled up her sleeves and set to work.

Squirt – rub, squirt – rub. With every flick of her duster hours of painstaking effort were swept away.

All Maisie could do was cower in a corner.

A few minutes later she heard the sound of a second key in the lock, and this time it really was the professor. Thank goodness! How Maisie hoped he'd notice that all the wonderful webs she'd made him were gone. This was his chance to say how much he'd liked them; to shake his fist and warn the intruder that if she came about the place in future, he'd send for the police.

But Maisie was in for a disappointment.

'Ah, my dear Mrs Mop, you've started the spring-cleaning!' the professor beamed. 'I see a wonderful difference already.'

'You did let it get into a state, Professor. But I'll get things shipshape. Off you go into the kitchen and drink your tea while I finish. There's only the study to do now.'

The study door opened. 'Oh dearie, dearie me. More cobwebs!' The woman flicked her duster and that was the end of the web on the anglepoise lamp. But Maisie was so upset by the professor's cruel words, it hardly seemed to matter. He had betrayed her. He had given this Mrs Mop more appreciation in five minutes than Maisie had had in a lifetime.

'Eugh! A dirty spider.' Not content with attacking works of art, the woman turned on Maisie.

SWOOSH. Next thing the spider knew she was out in the garden. Evicted. While the professor went on calmly drinking his tea.

Maisie felt as if her whole world had fallen apart.

'I gave that man the best months of my life,' she moaned. 'And this is the thanks I get. If I was a scorpion, I'd climb up the drainpipe into his bath and sting him.'

A sparrow in the nearby hedge started to laugh.

'That wouldn't help,' it chirped.

'Why not?' said Maisie.

'Because he still wouldn't admire your webs.'

It was true. The spider curled up into a sad little ball.

'So what are you going to do now?' chirped the sparrow.

'Nothing,' said Maisie.

'Don't be silly. You weren't made to do nothing. You were made to spin webs. The problem is you've been spinning them for the wrong person. You're meant to spin for your Maker – not Professor Brown.'

And with that the sparrow flew away.

Suddenly Maisie found herself climbing – scaling twigs and leaves until she reached the spot in the hedge where the bird had been.

Thoughtfully she dropped a silken thread. It floated for a moment then attached itself to a nearby stem. 'Spin for your Maker.' She remembered the sparrow's words. So Maisie spun. And when, at last, the final thread was in place she curled up in the centre of the web. 'This one's for you,' she yawned, and then she fell asleep.

The sparrow trilling at the top of its voice woke her next morning.

What a racket! 'I suppose he's singing for his Maker,' Maisie thought sleepily. 'But I wish he'd do it more quietly.' At the same time she couldn't help wondering what exactly was filling the bird with such delight.

'Come and see. Come and see,' the sparrow trilled.

So the spider joined him on his perch. And there, in the spot she'd just vacated, she saw something quite amazing: her web – transformed by dewdrops – sparkling and shimmering in the sun.

Just then the door of the house opened. The professor peered out and yes, he'd seen it too. He took off his spectacles, polished them, and returned them to his nose for a second look.

At long last Maisie's work had captured his attention. 'Beautiful! Quite beautiful!' he said.

SUGGESTED SONGS:

Father, we adore You (JP 44) (K 57)

If I were a butterfly (JP 94) (CPW 107) (K 128)

In our work and in our play (JP 108)

It's a happy day and I praise God for the weather (JP 118)

I want to live for Jesus ev'ry day (JP 122)

The greatest thing in all my life is knowing You (JP 239)

I want to love You, Lord (JP 374)

Noisy and the Hens

LENGTH: 7–8 minutes

TEACHING POINT: God is a forgiving father.

BIBLE READING: Luke 15:11–24

The master rose from the table and put his cap on. He was off to work. 'On guard, Noisy,' he said to the dog at his feet. Noisy's tail dropped between her legs. Sadly she trotted out of the kitchen to the yard.

The master needed a dog to guard his hen-run, and Noisy had been chosen for the job. Although having a special job had made her happy to begin with, now it was getting her down. The master's hens were hard work. All they ever did was fuss, flap and squabble.

'Grr. Stop that!' she growled at a group who were pecking at the wire.

'Go away. You're a spoilsport, Noisy,' they squawked back.

The hens squawked back like that at her all the time. They weren't in the least bit grateful for being guarded. If only they knew how Noisy wished she could go away. It was such a lovely afternoon, full of fresh spring smells. Oh to be out there, racing through fields!

With a sigh she lay down, her nose between her paws. Then, suddenly, above the squawking of the hens, she heard a voice.

'Hello there, Noisy. You look fed up.'

Who could it be? Noisy looked up and there, in the tree above her head, was a fat grey cuckoo staring down at her.

'Grr,' Noisy growled. Next to hens, cuckoos were her least favourite birds. Lazy mischief-makers, that was how she saw them. Always going around laying their eggs in other birds' nests.

But this cuckoo refused to take the hint. 'Cuckoo! I bet you wish you could go off for a run in the fields.' It cocked its head and winked a beady bright eye. 'It's a cuckoo-shame, that's what it is. You stuck here, having to guard all those foul fowl, on a cuckoo-lovely afternoon like this.'

'It's my job,' said Noisy. 'I do it for the master. He'll take me for a run as soon as he gets home.'

'Taking his time, isn't he though?' said the cuckoo. 'Still, I suppose he'll come back when it cuckoo-suits him. A hard taskmaster, that's what he is. All the other guard dogs get a cuckoo-run in the afternoon.'

'Do they?' Noisy pricked up her ears.

'Tell you what,' said the cuckoo brightly. 'You trot off and I'll guard the hens. Your master needn't know a thing about it. He'll be happy. You'll be happy. What could be cuckoo-better? Right?'

Wrong. Noisy knew the master wouldn't want her trusting her special job to a cuckoo. Still, it was very tempting. . . .

'He needn't know a cuckoo-thing about it.' It was as if the bird had read her thoughts. 'You'll be back long before him. Able to slobber round him just as usual. Go on! What are you cuckoo-waiting for? I'll take cuckoo-care of things.'

'Oh all right,' said Noisy, and away she went, leaping and bounding, through the farmyard gate and out into the countryside beyond. On she ran, through field after field, until finally she flopped down, panting under a tree.

It had been a good run. But she missed her master. She got up, sniffed around for a bit and then decided to go home.

'He needn't know a thing about it,' she reminded herself as she went.

She couldn't help feeling uneasy though. What if he suspected something? Noisy knew she must try and behave just as usual when he came. But her tail felt all droopy. What if he noticed that she wasn't greeting him with her usual faster-than-the-speed-of-lightning waggle?

Her uneasiness grew as she trotted through the gate into the yard. Something was wrong. She sniffed the ground. Yes. Definitely. She smelt an enemy smell in the dust. And everything seemed so quiet. Not a squawk…not a flap…not a squabble….

'Things OK here?' She pattered across to the hen-run and looked inside. A terrible sight met her eyes. Disaster! There was a hole in the wire. A scattering of feathers. And not a hen to be seen. Noisy raised her nose to the air and howled. Why oh why had she ever trusted that lying cuckoo? He'd talked her into deserting her post and now the hen-run had been raided by a fox.

The guard dog had never felt so ashamed and frightened in all her life. The master's hens had been eaten, and the master would be back any minute. There was only one thing for it. She would have to run away.

So, for the second time that day, Noisy ran off into the fields. Only this time she knew she could never come home. On and on she ran through field after field until the sun was low in the sky, and she felt so tired and miserable that she just tumbled under a clump of bushes and fell asleep.

The master's voice woke her up. 'Noisy! Noisy!' He had come looking for her. Her heart leapt. Then she remembered the empty run. How angry he must be! She peeked out under the bushes and saw that he was carrying a nasty-looking stick.

'Noisy! Noisy!' he called again.

She was ashamed. She was frightened. But the sound of his voice was like a magnet drawing her to him. Hearing it, she knew she couldn't spend the rest of her life roaming the fields with nothing to do and no one to bark for. She wanted to be the master's dog again – yes, even if it meant a beating.

She crept from her hiding-place. She put her nose between her paws and whined.

In an instant he was by her side. She stiffened, waiting for the whack of his stick on her back. But instead she felt a gentle, stroking hand. She opened her eyes and, to her amazement, saw joy, not anger, on his face. 'Little dog with a big bark,' he said. 'I'm glad to have you back.'

And this was only the first surprise. The second was waiting for her back at the farmyard. There was the hen-run, just as she had left it. Broken. Empty. Smelling of fox. 'Nothing to guard here,' the master said gently.

But there was something going on in the farmhouse kitchen. Even before the master put his key in the lock, Noisy heard the wonderful sound. Fussing … flapping … squabbling. … The door opened and yes! Her tail practically took off with delight. There were hens squawking everywhere: on the table, under the chairs, on top of the cooker. There was even a plump Rhode Island Red in her basket!

'Where did you get to, Noisy?' it flapped. 'If the master hadn't come home in time to save us we'd have been eaten by the fox.'

'Serves you right,' Noisy almost barked – and then stopped. After all, she hadn't got what she deserved. And she was really, truly glad the hens were safe.

'Three cheers for the master!' she barked instead.

'Cluck-cluck-hurrah! Cluck-cluck-hurrah!' There followed a few moments of total uproar.

Then Noisy stopped chasing around like a mad thing and the room fell silent.

'Sorry I left you … .'

'Sorry we were rude … .'

And that was it. All safe. All sorry. With a sigh of relief the dog leapt into her basket and licked the Rhode Island Red on the beak.

SUGGESTED SONGS:

God forgave my sin in Jesus' name (JP 54)

Stand up and bless the Lord your God (JP 224)

There is a green hill far away (JP 245) (K 725)

There's a way back to God from the dark paths of sin (JP 248)

You can't stop rain from falling down (JP 297) (K 796)

Every day if you go astray (JP 331)

God of all mercy (JP 350)

Grace is when God gives us (JP 355) (CPW 71) (K 92)

Lovejoy's Song

LENGTH: 6–7 minutes

TEACHING POINT: The meaning of the cross.

BIBLE READING: Luke 23:32–43

Lovejoy the Nightingale and Gossip the Mouse lived in a forest beside a clearing. The forest belonged to the king and queen. Every evening while Lovejoy flew up into the treetops to sing until dawn, Gossip would nibble crumbs in the royal dining-room. Then, when the king and queen came down for breakfast, he would hide behind a curtain and listen to what they said – which meant that he had lots of juicy gossip to pass on to the rest of the creatures when he arrived back in the clearing. For example, he might tell them that the king had had prunes for breakfast, or that the queen was planning to redecorate the royal dungeons. It was all a bit boring really … until one day the mouse brought really sensational news.

'Pack your bags, folks,' he squeaked. 'The king and queen are planning to chop down the royal forest.'

'I don't believe it!' Lovejoy gasped.

'It's as true as my whiskers,' Gossip assured her. 'The king wants money, so he's planning to sell the royal trees.'

'But surely … surely he could get money some other way,' cried Lovejoy.

'He could … but he won't,' squeaked the mouse. 'He's a greedy tyrant, and his wife's no better.'

'Hiss! Boo! Down with the monarchy!' By this time the rest of the forest creatures had heard the terrible news and they were hissing and booing and vowing to get their own back on the king and queen.

'Tomorrow I'll raid the royal hen-run,' vowed Fox.

'I'll nibble the royal roses,' vowed Rabbit.

'I'll make a humping great molehill in the middle of the royal croquet lawn,' vowed Mole.

And so it went on, with every forest creature saying what he or she was going to do. In the end Lovejoy was the only one who hadn't spoken. Suddenly she found that all the animals were looking at her. 'What will you do, Lovejoy?' they wanted to know.

Lovejoy was too shocked to think, never mind answer.

'Here's an idea,' said Gossip. 'Tonight when you sing in the treetops you could ask for lightning to strike the royal palace.'

'Hurrah! Nice one, Gossip!' all the animals cheered.

That night, as usual, Lovejoy flew up to the treetops. As usual she sang to the moon and the stars. But she didn't ask for lightning to strike the palace. Instead, as dawn broke, she finished with her usual song, which was actually a prayer:

> *Bless the king, bless the queen,*
> *Bless the knights and villagers,*
> *Bless every woodland creature*
> *From the greatest badger to the smallest bee.*

The animals did not like this.

'The king and queen are our enemies,' Fox scolded. 'How dare you bless them? From now on you must pray for lightning to strike the royal palace, otherwise we'll drive you from the forest.'

Well, that afternoon things went from bad to worse. Mole was hit on the head with a croquet ball. Rabbit was shot at by an angry gardener. Fox was chased from the royal hen-run by the royal hounds. Worst of all, a team of common woodcutters came and started chopping. . . .

It was with a heavy heart that Lovejoy flew to the treetops that evening. From her perch on the uppermost branch she could see the ugly gash in the side of the forest where the first trees had been felled. She could see the helpless creatures whose homes had been destroyed. She had a perfect view of the royal palace where the king and queen now dined.

'Greedy tyrants,' Lovejoy said to herself. 'It is true what Gossip says. Why should I bless them?'

She was just about to pray for lightning to strike the palace when she heard someone or something calling her name.

She glanced up, startled.

The moon was shining down on her. 'Look again, Songbird,' it whispered. 'Look into the clearing, and remember – love is stronger than hate.'

Once again the nightingale looked down from the treetops. And this time she saw something she hadn't noticed before. She saw a single cross-shaped tree standing on the edge of the grassy gap between the forest and palace.

'That's the shape of love,' the moon whispered.

Somehow, as Lovejoy gazed on the shape of love, a song of love took shape in her throat. It took a lot of courage to sing it, but she did so more sweetly than ever before in her life – not just once but over and over again all through the long dark hours until dawn:

> *Bless the king, bless the queen,*
> *Bless the knights and villagers,*
> *Bless every woodland creature*
> *From the greatest badger to the smallest bee.*

If the forest creatures had been put out to hear Lovejoy blessing the king and queen once, they were really mad now. 'Did you hear that?' they muttered and growled as they gathered in the clearing next morning.

'We'll drive the traitor away,' roared Fox. 'If she wants to bless tyrants, let her live in a cage in the palace.'

Meanwhile, in the royal dining-room the king and queen were having breakfast. 'My dear,' said the queen as she sprinkled sugar on the royal porridge, 'I have been thinking. I should rather you did not cut down the royal forest. You may sell the royal emeralds instead.'

The king dropped his spoon. 'Are you really asking me to sell your jewels and keep the forest trees?'

Thoughtfully the queen nodded. 'It's because of something that happened last night. There was a bird – a nightingale – singing in the forest. I've never heard anything so lovely. And it suddenly struck me that if the forest were chopped down, the bird would go too. And I should never hear that song again. . . .'

'In that case,' the king beamed, 'the forest is safe.' He was about to kiss his wife's cheek when suddenly she screamed! (Can you guess why?)

The mouse didn't stop to pay his respects. 'The forest is safe. ... The forest is safe. . . .'

He shot straight out of the royal dining-room and back to the clearing.

Within minutes he was spreading the wonderful news.

So it turned out that when Lovejoy finally flew down from the treetops she didn't find a crowd of jeering creatures waiting to drive her from the forest but a crowd of cheering creatures all begging her to stay – which made her so happy she flew straight up onto a branch of the cross-shaped tree and burst into song, while down below Gossip continued to shriek at the top of his squeaker.

'Hate – bad. Love – good. Lovejoy's song has saved the wood.'

NOTE: This story could be used in the context of caring for the environment or as an illustration of the power of prayer.

SUGGESTED SONGS:

I'm singing for my Lord ev'rywhere I go (JP 105)

Jesus is Lord! Creation's voice proclaims it (JP 137)

Make me a channel of Your peace (JP 161) (K 248)

Morning has broken (JP 166) (CPW 154)

O Lord my God! When I in awesome wonder (JP 179)

On Calvary's tree He died for me (JP 183) (K 271)

Saviour of the world, thank You for dying on the cross (JP 216)

When I survey the wondrous cross (JP 277)

Empty the Bubblewand

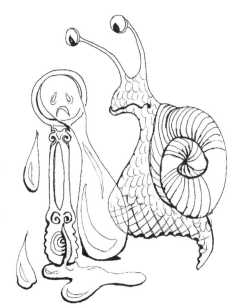

LENGTH: 6–7 minutes. Tell this story using drawings of a bubblewand and the forest creatures. Blow real bubbles at the end.

TEACHING POINT: Christians are meant to produce spiritual fruit. The Holy Spirit makes love … joy … peace … goodness, and so on, flow from our lives.

BIBLE READING: Acts 2:1–4; Galatians 5:16–24

Empty the Bubblewand lay in a muddy patch feeling confused and lonely. (A bubblewand, by the way, is a small piece of plastic shaped to look like a round, empty head, supported by a pencil-thin body.) He'd lain there ever since his owner had come to play in the forest and dropped him from her pocket. As a result of the fall he'd lost his memory. He couldn't remember where he'd come from or who he belonged to. All he knew was his name and what he did.

It was a great relief to hear someone or something beside him on the path.

'Hello! Hello! I'm Empty the Bubblewand,' he called loudly. 'Who are you?'

The passerby stopped nibbling the grass around the muddy patch, hopped over and sniffed round Empty's head.

'I'm Scholar the Rabbit,' he said. 'What did you say your name was?'

'Empty the Bubblewand,' replied Empty. 'I make bubbles, you know.'

'Well I never. How interesting!' Scholar took a closer sniff.

And with that who should come along but Scholar's friend Gossip the Mouse.

Empty was overjoyed at the prospect of more company. As soon as Gossip came within earshot he called out. 'Hello, Mouse. Come and join in the fun.'

Before Gossip could ask 'What fun?' Scholar said knowledgeably, 'Gossip, I'd like you to meet our new friend, Empty the Bubblewand. He makes bubbles, you know.'

'Oh yes! I see. Very nice,' Gossip squeaked.

He was just about to tell Empty how pleased he was to meet him and how he'd always planned to make bubbles himself, if only he could find the time, when along came Slow the Snail.

'Hello, Snail. You're just in time for the party. How are you keeping?' called Empty, scarcely able to believe his good luck.

'I've been worse,' said Slow. And then, slowly, he lowered his antlered head and stared. 'But who are you?'

'This is Empty the Bubblewand,' squeaked Gossip.

'He makes bubbles, you know,' explained Scholar.

Slow took another long look. And then, since he wasn't as good-natured as Scholar or as easily impressed as Gossip, he came out with a very awkward question.

'I don't see any bubbles,' he said. 'Where are they?'

Scholar wiggled his ears at Gossip. Gossip twitched his nose at Scholar. And you could see they were both wondering the same thing.

As for Empty, he was so shocked, he hardly knew what to say. It was his way of getting attention – telling strangers who he was and what he did. He hadn't bargained for anyone expecting the bubbles to be real.

'I've lost my instructions . . .' he muttered in the end.

Scholar's nose twitched confidently. 'In that case, if you'll just come along with us, we'll take you to someone who's sure to have an answer to your problem.'

And the someone Scholar, Gossip and Slow took Empty to see was Hoot the Wise Owl.

'What can I dooo for yooo?' Hoot hooted when they all appeared at the foot of his tree.

'This is Empty the Bubblewand,' explained Scholar. 'But he's lost his instructions. So we were wondering if you could tell him how to make bubbles.'

Hoot looked at Empty over his spectacles. Then he disappeared into his tree and came back a few minutes later with a glass full of green liquid.

'Bubble mixtooore,' he hooted. 'All Empty needs to dooo is plunge head-first into that glass so that the liquid fills his head or his heart or whatever he calls that hole at the centre of his person.'

'That's easy,' snuffled Scholar. 'Thank you so much, Hoot. Well, come on Empty. What are you waiting for?'

Poor Empty! He was wishing he'd never met Scholar or Gossip or Slow – and most of all he was wishing he'd never met Hoot. The mixture in the glass looked all wet and sticky. The last thing he wanted to do was plunge head-first into it.

'Perhaps Empty doesn't want to make bubbles after all,' said the owl.

That did it. 'Oh yes I do,' said Empty. And – splash – into the glass he went.

When he came out a few seconds later, he was almost beside himself with excitement. 'That was wonderful,' he cried. 'The most wonderful experience of my whole life. I feel great. And look, I'm not muddy any more. And my middle isn't empty. Thank you, oh thank you, Hoot, for telling me how to become a real bubblewand.'

Scholar and Gossip frisked around with delight, but Slow was looking as puzzled as ever.

'I don't see any bubbles,' he said.

Oh dear! For a moment everyone looked as if they'd like to give the snail a good kick on the shell. And then a green liquid tear dripped down Empty's stick. 'Slow's right,' he told Hoot sadly. 'It hasn't worked. There still aren't any bubbles.'

'There's one more thing to be done,' said the owl. 'Now that your middle's full of bubble mixtooore, we must hang you upside-down from the branch of a tree and wait for the wind to blow through.'

By this time Empty would have done anything – anything at all – to make bubbles.

'It'll be worth it,' he whispered to Scholar as they hauled him up into a branch and left him hanging.

'I hope,' he added quietly as the creatures moved back from the tree.

For a long moment nothing happened.

And then – suddenly – there was a whispering, a rustling, a stirring of the leaves and – whoosh – a cloud of the most beautiful bubbles streamed from Empty's hole.

'Hurrah!' cheered Scholar and Gossip. Slow didn't say anything. He just slithered after the biggest bubble and tried to catch it on his antlers.

'More bubble mixtoore! Quick! Fill up. Fill up,' Hoot hooted.

And – whoosh – as the wind sent another cloud of sparkling balls dancing through the clearing, Empty thought he would explode with joy. To think he'd been calling himself a bubblewand all this time and never known what it meant until now!

'I'm a BUBBLEWAND. I make BUBBLES,' he cried. 'Look, Gossip! Look, Slow! I'm being it. I'm making bubbles. I'm being what I've always said I am!'

SUGGESTED SONGS:

Keep me shining, Lord (JP 147)

Lord dismiss us with Your blessing (JP 155)

Love, joy, peace and patience, kindness (JP 158)

Peace, I give to you, I give to you my peace (JP 196)

Spirit of the living God (JP 222)

Wherever I am I will praise You, Lord (JP 283)

Love, joy, peace (JP 425)

Spirit of God, please fill me now to overflowing (JP 465)

Dr Good and the Strangers

LENGTH: 6 minutes. This story works as a mime. (five people plus the narrator.)

TEACHING POINT: Jesus forgives sin and makes sin-damaged lives whole. What sort of things can hold us back from receiving that new life?

BIBLE READING: John 3:16–21; 1 John 1:9

Dr Good was a very famous doctor. People came to him for treatment from all over the world.

One day he arrived home to find two ugly great sacks propped up outside the front door.

'I'll have to speak to Hugh about that. We don't want him dumping rubbish on the doorstep,' he said to his wife.

'It's nothing to do with Hugh,' Mrs Good replied. 'Those sacks belong to two patients who are waiting to see you in the surgery.'

'Patients! I wasn't expecting any patients,' the doctor frowned. 'Did you get their names?'

'I *tried* to. But there's a bit of a language problem. As far as I can make out they're called He-man and She-man. Actually,' Mrs Good lowered her voice, 'they're rather strange.'

Sure enough, a few moments later, Dr Good was greeted by two of the strangest-looking strangers he'd ever met in his life. They were a man and a woman. Both had long straggly hair. Both wore dirty ragged animal skins. And both were so stooped, their hands almost touched the floor as they walked.

'It's those sacks that did the damage,' Mrs Good whispered. 'Poor things! By the look of it they've been carrying them all their lives.'

The doctor's heart went out to the couple. At the same time he felt confident he could help them. He'd seen worse cases than this.

Just as his wife had warned, though, language was a problem. He-man and She-man seemed to understand him. But he couldn't understand them. For several minutes he struggled to find out where they'd come from. In the end he gave up.

He sat down at his desk and called up a special program on his computer.

'Watch this,' he told his patients.

A few clicks and he summoned two figures onto the screen – stooped figures, with obvious back problems. Just for good measure he added in straggly hair and rags.

He-man and She-man gave little gasps of recognition and pointed to each other.

'That's right. It's you,' the doctor nodded. 'The way you are today. But look what I can do.'

Click ... click ... The figures straightened up. *Click*. Off with the rags. *Clickety click*. Away they went, running and leaping across the screen.

'Fantasmibosh!' cheered He-man.

It wasn't too hard to work out what that word meant. 'Here's something even more fantasmibosh,' Dr Good smiled. 'What you've just seen on the screen can happen to you in real life. Patients from all over the world have come to me stooped, often scarcely able to walk – and they have gone away leaping and running.'

He passed two forms across the desk.

'All you need to do is sign these forms and then I can begin treatment.'

He-man lifted a pen.

'Of course,' the doctor added, 'you'll have to stop carrying those sacks.'

What! He-man looked over at She-man, and suddenly seemed to have second thoughts.

'Noop,' he frowned and set the pen down again.

'Noop.' She-man followed his lead.

'It will be worth it, you know,' Dr Good urged. He went over to the filing cabinet and returned with a photograph. 'Look. Here's a picture of a patient before treatment. You can see for yourselves how bent he is. But today he's fit and active. In fact he's outside working in our garden. If you like I'll call him in so he can tell you himself what a wonderful difference my treatment has made.'

Still He-man and She-man shook their heads.

'Perhaps they're worried about money,' suggested Mrs Good. 'Maybe they carry sacks for a living. Maybe they're afraid they won't be able to pay you.'

Was that it? 'My friends, you mustn't let money stand in your way,' the doctor cried. 'It's true, the treatment *is* costly, but I'm offering it free.'

Now He-man and She-man seemed pulled in two directions. First they would gaze with apparent longing at the screen, where the leaping figures still ran to and fro. Then they would hobble over to the window and look out at their sacks.

'Whatever you've got in there, it surely can't mean more to you than your future.'

But apparently it did.

Suddenly She-man couldn't bear to watch the figures any longer. She switched off the computer while He-man crumpled the form into a little ball and threw it onto the floor.

There was nothing more to be said.

'They're killing themselves. What a tragedy!' Dr Good muttered as he watched the couple go.

'There's still a chance they'll change their minds. Look! Hugh is talking to them,' Mrs Good pointed out.

Hopefully the Goods looked on while the gardener pleaded with the couple to come back with him into the house. To no avail. He-man and She-man heaved their sacks onto their backs and staggered off down the drive.

'Have you any idea where they come from?' the doctor asked Hugh when they'd gone.

'Well, yes Boss. They come from the same place as me – the land of Bent-over-double. Everyone in Bent-over-double is bent double under a sack.'

'But why on earth do people want to carry heavy sacks around with them the whole time? What do they keep in them? Their life savings?'

The gardener smiled sadly. 'No, Boss. Bent-over-doublers fills their sacks with the things they's ashamed of – the things they don't want other folks to see.'

'You mean He-man and She-man refused treatment because they were afraid I might open their sacks?'

'That's right,' Hugh nodded. 'But there was another reason. In Bent-over-double everyone has a sack and everyone is crooked. They're afraid of being different from their friends.'

SUGGESTED SONGS:

Lord Jesus Christ, You have come to us (JP 156)

Oh! Oh! Oh! how good is the Lord (JP 180) (K 266)

Search me, O God, and know my heart today (JP 212)

There's new life in Jesus, Lift up your heart (JP 249)

Though the world has forsaken God (JP 257)

All you have to do is to ask the Lord (JP 307)

I've come to a time when I must change (JP 383)

The Three Trees

LENGTH: 4–5 minutes

TEACHING POINT: God accomplished his plan for the world through Jesus. In Jesus we find his perfect plan for our lives.

BIBLE READING: Ephesians 1:1–14

Once upon a time there were three trees growing side by side in the forest. They were friends. And just the way friends do, they used to spend their time chatting together. And just the way it is with most friends, even though they were all more or less the same height, and they were all growing in the same place, they were all different.

The first tree loved beauty.

The second tree loved adventure.

And the third tree loved God.

Anyway one day the trees were talking about what they wanted to be when they grew up.

'When I grow up I want to be a carved treasure chest, filled with sparkling jewels,' the first tree said.

The second tree didn't think much of this. 'When I grow up I want to be a strong ship,' it said. 'And my captain will be a great explorer and together we'll discover new lands.'

Meanwhile the third tree was shaking its branches. 'I don't want to be made into anything,' it said. 'I want to stay right here growing taller every year. I want to be the tallest tree in the forest. Then when people look at me they'll see I'm pointing them to God.'

The years went by and one day three woodcutters arrived in the forest.

'At last!' cried the first tree as the first woodcutter cut it down. 'My dream of becoming a treasure chest is about to come true.'

'Brilliant!' cried the second tree as the second woodcutter cut it down. 'My dream of becoming a sailing ship is about to come true.'

'Oh no!' cried the third tree as the third woodcutter cut it down. 'Now I won't be able to point people to God.'

The woodcutters carried the three trees away. And for two of them, at any rate, the future looked bright. But before long all three had said goodbye to their earlier plans. Instead of being made into a beautiful treasure chest, the first tree was made into an ugly feeding-box for animals. And instead of being made into a fine sailing ship, the second tree was made into a simple fishing boat. As for the third tree, it wasn't made into anything at all. It was just cut up into planks and left stacked in the builder's yard.

Life went on. The years went by. And gradually the three trees learnt to live with their broken dreams.

Then one cold winter's night, everything changed for the first tree. A baby was born – clearly no ordinary child. Angels sang. Shepherds and kings came to visit him.

And guess which animal feed-box his mother used as a cradle?

You know, when the first tree realised what had happened, its heart filled with joy. 'My dreams have come true after all,' it said. 'I may not have been filled with gold and jewels. But I have held the greatest treasure on earth.'

Many more years passed – about thirty altogether – and finally, one day, everything changed for the second tree. There it was out in the middle of a lake when a terrible storm blew up. The wind was so strong and the waves so high that the little tree was sure it was going to sink. And then something incredible happened. One of the men it was carrying stood up. 'Peace! Be still,' he said to the wind and the waves. And they obeyed him.

And when the second tree realised what had happened, its heart filled with joy. 'My dreams have come true after all,' it said. 'I may not have carried a great explorer, but I have carried the Maker of heaven and earth.'

It wasn't too long after that that things changed for the third tree. At last a carpenter came and took it away. But to the tree's dismay he didn't make it into anything beautiful. Nor did he make it into anything useful. Instead he made it into a coarse wooden cross.

'This is the sort of cross soldiers use to put criminals to death,' the tree thought in horror.

Sure enough, the tree found itself carried to the place of execution. And there, at the top of a hill, a man was nailed to its cross-beam and left to die.

It should have been absolutely the worst day of the tree's life – except for one thing. The man hanging there in agony was no ordinary criminal paying the punishment for his crime. He was Jesus – the Son of God – dying for the sins of the world.

And when the third tree realised what had happened its heart thrilled with joy.

'My dreams have come true after all,' it said. 'I may not be the tallest tree in the forest. But from this day on, as the cross of Christ, I shall always point people towards God.'

SUGGESTED SONGS:

Come and praise the Lord our King (JP 34)

God is working His purpose out (JP 57)

I do not know what lies ahead (JP 92)

Now the green blade riseth from the buried grain (JP 174)

Oh, the love that drew salvation's plan (JP 181)

With Jesus in the boat we can smile at the storm (JP 291)

The Most Important Job

LENGTH: 8 minutes

TEACHING POINT: The importance of serving and worshipping God.

BIBLE READING: Colossians 3:22

Once upon a time there were four trainee angels known as 'the Sparklers'. Emerald, the first angel, had been training for four thousand years and wore a gleaming emerald sash. Ruby, the second angel, had been training for three thousand years and wore a shimmering ruby sash. Sapphire, the third angel, had been training for two thousand years and wore a twinkling sapphire sash. The fourth angel was called Pebble and he wore a woolly hat.

One day Shining Light, their angel coach, set the Sparklers a challenge. 'I want you to fly to earth and find people who are doing important jobs,' she said. 'Begin the challenge when you hear me blow my horn once – like this.' She blew one sweet sharp blast. 'And keep gathering information until you hear the "time's up" horn. Then come straight back to heaven and there'll be a prize for the angel who has found the most important job.'

Shining Light flew off, and the Sparklers all hopped up and down with excitement. 'We must fly to the four corners of the earth,' cried Emerald. 'So Sapphire, you go South. Ruby can go West. I shall go East, and that leaves Pebble to go North.'

'Errr… which way is North?' Pebble blinked round.

The sound of Shining Light's horn stopped their chat. 'That's it. I'm off,' cried Emerald, and away she went. 'See you later,' cried Sapphire and Ruby and away they went too. Pebble waited until his three friends had turned into specks in the distance and vanished from sight. Then slowly he pulled on his woolly hat and flew off in the direction he hoped was North.

Before long the surface of the earth came into view. Pebble peered down worriedly. It was all right for the other Sparklers. Emerald, Sapphire and Ruby loved challenges. They always seemed to know exactly what to do. But Pebble's brain didn't work as quickly as theirs. 'Think, Pebble, think…' he told himself. 'You're looking for a person doing an important job… hey, wait a minute… Important jobs are done by important people… Kings and Queens and Presidents and Prime Ministers… the sort of people who live in palaces and castles…'

So he flew on, trying to spot a castle or palace. The trouble was he was battling against a cold North wind. It made his eyes water so much he could hardly see, and his wings so tired he could hardly fly. Soon he just had to flutter down into a car park. He touched the ground as two children were getting out of a car. Quickly Pebble folded his wings out of sight, and went over to them.

'Hello,' he said politely. 'I need to meet someone important. Are there any castles or palaces around here?'

'The nearest castle is fifty miles away,' said the boy. 'But we're going to meet someone very important in that hall over there.' He pointed to a building beside the carpark.

'That's right,' said his sister. 'Come with us and meet with the King of Kings.'

'The King of Kings! Wow!' gasped Pebble, hardly believing his good luck. For once in his life he was going to beat Emerald, Ruby and Sapphire. Being King of Kings had to be the world's most important job.....

'Wow!' he gasped again as they went in through the door. At the front he saw a low platform and a piano. At the back he saw grown-ups handing out juice and biscuits.

'Imagine! The King of Kings coming to an ordinary little hall like this!' Pebble marvelled. Then he sat down beside his new friends and waited for the King to arrive. There was some singing and Pebble joined in, praising God at the top of his voice. Time passed. The children heard a Bible story and then they sang some more.

'Has the King been delayed then?' Pebble asked the boy.

'Delayed? Don't be silly!' the boy laughed. 'He's right here with us. Don't you know the King of Kings is another name for God?'

Oh dear! Pebble should have known that. 'I got mixed up. I thought you were talking about a human King,' he moaned. And with that he heard a sound that made his heart sink. Nobody else in the hall heard it. But to Pebble's angel ears, the sound of Shining Light's horn was as clear as a bell. The angel leader was blowing the 'time's up' call. It was too late now for Pebble to find anyone doing an important job. He'd failed. Failed miserably. And now he must head back to heaven and explain.....

Seconds later, feeling very silly, Pebble slouched alongside the other Sparklers waiting to give his report.

'Buck up, Pebble,' Emerald hissed in his ear. 'Here comes Shining Light.'

And with a swish of wings and a radiant glow, the angelic leader appeared...

'Now let's hear about the people you found,' said Shining Light. 'Emerald, you go first.'

Immediately Emerald whipped a thick ball of blue yarn out from under her wing. 'I've brought this yarn from a hospital, high up in the mountains of Nepal,' she said. 'There I found a doctor who was caring for leprosy patients, giving them treatment to make their illness better. Some who would otherwise have lost the use of their hands were learning to knit with yarn like this. I think that doctor is doing a most important job.'

No sooner had she finished than Sapphire pulled a pair of handcuffs from under her wing.

'I brought these handcuffs back from a big city in America. There I found a policeman catching a car thief and helping to keep the streets safe. I think that policeman is doing a most important job.'

Next it was Ruby's turn. Eagerly she took a green branch of a tree out from under her wing. 'I flew to the Australian outback,' she cried. 'When I arrived, there was a blazing fire. I saw a firefighter, his face black with smoke, turning his hose on the flames. Before I left he had helped to put out the fire and this is a branch from one of the trees that was saved. I think that firefighter does a most important job.'

There was a moment of silence and they all looked at Pebble who was wishing he could fly off and hide in a cloud. 'I got mixed up,' he stammered. 'I spent the afternoon with some children in a church hall. We had juice and heard a Bible story and sang and prayed to God.'

As Pebble said this, he could hear the other Sparklers giggling, the way they often did when he got confused.

'So which of the people we found is doing the most important job?' Emerald burst out. 'Which of us has won the prize?'

Shining Light smiled. 'You all did very well, but we do have a winner.'

At these words Emerald, Sapphire and Ruby held their breath and Pebble studied the pearl studded floor.

'What makes a job important isn't so much who does it or what the job is,' Shining Light went on. 'What makes a job important is who that job is done for... and no-one can do anything for anyone more important than the Creator God... which means the prize must go to the Sparkler who found children and grown-ups worshipping him.'

'But... but... but that Sparkler was ME?' Pebble gasped.

'That's right.' From under her wing Shining Light produced a beautiful golden star. 'Wear this as a reminder that the most important jobs are done for God by folk who love him.' And she pinned the golden star to Pebble's hat.

SUGGESTED SONGS:

He's great! He's God (JP 79)

King of kings and Lord of lords (JP 148)

My God is so big (JP 169) (CPW 157) (K 255)

Come on and celebrate (JP 325) (CPW 26) (K 34)

Lord we've come to worship You (JP 422) (CPW 147)

What a mighty God we serve (JP 491)

PART TWO

ACROSS THE CENTURIES

Polycarp

LENGTH: 4–5 minutes

TEACHING POINT: Jesus can strengthen us to witness faithfully even through persecution.

BIBLE READING: Matthew 10:17–31

Bishop Polycarp of Smyrna had known for some time that his life was at risk, and sure enough, one day a large posse of police arrived to arrest him. The first thing the old man did was ask whether they would like some supper after their long journey.

This came as a shock to the arresting officer. He'd heard some terrible stories about Christians – about how they ate babies and drank their blood. He'd come expecting to round up a dangerous criminal, only to be faced with this harmless-looking fellow.

He was in a bit of a dither for the rest of the evening, especially when Polycarp asked if he might pray for an hour before leaving. All this calmness was disturbing. Prisoners weren't meant to be calm. In the end he gave the old man an extra hour to finish his prayers. (Christians had a hundred and one brothers and sisters to pray for, it seemed.) Then he got hold of a donkey (the fellow would never have managed the journey on foot). And, after a final prayer from Polycarp and a final cup of wine for everyone else, they set off into the night.

Dawn was breaking when Herod, the chief of police met them on the outskirts of the city. He too was taken aback when he clapped eyes on such an inoffensive-looking prisoner. He called Polycarp over.

'Come up here into my chariot and I'll give you a word of advice,' he said. He'd no love for Christians, but he didn't particularly want this one to be put to death – especially when there was such a simple way of avoiding it. The emperor had said Christians shouldn't be executed without first being given a chance to deny their faith. All this innocent-looking man had to do was say 'Caesar is Lord', sacrifice to the Roman gods, and he could walk free.

'It's quite straightforward, you know.' He placed an encouraging hand on Polycarp's bony shoulder. 'You just repeat three little words and throw the tiniest pinch of incense on the altar. And that's it! So what do you say?'

Polycarp didn't answer.

Thinking he hadn't understood, Herod went over the whole thing again.

This time the prisoner looked him straight in the face. His voice was quavery but clear. 'I won't be taking your advice,' he said.

'Very well. Have it your own way,' Herod snorted. He was a busy man and he'd already wasted enough time on this prisoner. 'Take the silly old fool to the amphitheatre!' he ordered.

The amphitheatre was a huge oval building at the heart of the city. There Polycarp was brought before Quartus, the governor.

Like the police and the police chief, Quartus took one look at him and decided to do his best to get him off the hook. 'There's nothing to fear if you're prepared to be sensible,' he explained. 'And I'm sure you will be sensible … after all, you owe yourself a bit of peace and quiet.' Then he asked Polycarp to repeat a little phrase – *away with the atheists* – designed to show he disapproved of Christians.

Polycarp turned and glanced round the crowded arena, shuddering slightly at the sight of so many hostile faces. Atheists, to the governor, might have been Christians who refused to worship the Roman gods, but to Polycarp, atheists were people who didn't believe in the one true God. He looked up to heaven and then back at the restless mob.

'Away with the atheists,' he said.

'Good!' Quartus smiled, taking this as a sign that the prisoner was prepared to be reasonable.

'There's just one more thing before you go,' he said smoothly. 'All you need to do now is curse Christ.'

He made it sound so trivial – as if the curse was little more than a casual greeting. But the prisoner's reply wiped the smile off his face.

'For eighty-six years I have been Christ's servant and he has done me no wrong,' Polycarp said simply. 'How can I blaspheme against my King and Saviour?'

Eighty-six years! Of course Quartus had known the man was old. That was the very reason they'd all been trying to spare him. But now … well … the governor shook his head. There was nothing more to be said. If the old fool insisted on signing his own death warrant so be it. There was no way he could cover this up, or sweep it under the couch.

'Tell the crowd Polycarp has confessed he is a Christian,' he ordered the herald.

Polycarp has confessed he is a Christian. The news was out. And the mob went wild.

'Kill the destroyer of our gods!' they yelled.

'Set the wild animals upon him.'

'No, let him be destroyed by flames.'

Within minutes they were rushing from the arena to collect logs and brushwood for the fire.

Quietly Polycarp prepared to become the oldest Christian martyr. He showed no fear as he took off his sandals and allowed himself to be tied to the stake.

His death was a triumph – the climax of eighty-six years of following his Master.

And the Christian church was strengthened by his faith.

EXTRA INFORMATION:

Christians were persecuted periodically during the first three centuries until the Emperor Galerius was forced to sign an edict of toleration on his deathbed in 311 AD and Constantine and Licinius signed the Edict of Milan in 313 AD. St Polycarp was born around 69 AD and died around 155 AD. He was the Greek bishop of Smyrna (modern Turkey) and a personal disciple of St John the Evangelist.

SUGGESTED SONGS:

At the name of Jesus (JP 13)

Father, hear the prayer we offer (JP 41)

He who would valiant be (JP 80) (CPW 82)

I sing a song of the saints of God (JP 115)

Now be strong and very courageous (JP 172)

Saviour of the world, thank You for dying on the cross (JP 216)

Christ be my leader by night as by day (JP 319)

I'm going to stand up, I'm going to stand up (JP 380)

Possessions

LENGTH: 5–6 minutes

TEACHING POINT: True freedom comes from belonging to God.

BIBLE READING: John 17:6–19; Malachi 3:17

Nobody meeting Brigid for the first time would ever have guessed she was a slave. She'd such a happy air of freedom. Once, when she was minding the sheep, a beggar asked her for help. She didn't have any money, but she couldn't bear to send him away empty-handed. So she gave him one of her master's sheep. On another occasion she was cooking five pieces of bacon for five guests when a dog came and whined at her feet. The guests looked perfectly well fed, but the dog was starving. You can guess what happened to the fifth piece of bacon.

Needless to say, this kind of behaviour didn't go down well with Brigid's mistress.

'The girl's a menace. Get rid of her!' she ordered her husband, Dubthach.

Tradition has it that Dubthach was actually Brigid's father. But he certainly wasn't the sort of dad you could rely on in a crisis. Brigid's mother had been his bondwoman (or slave) and he'd already sold her. Now he reckoned he'd get no peace until he'd done the same with Brigid.

The girl was working at the quern on the day he decided to make the sale (a quern was a heavy stone contraption used to grind corn).

'Gather your things and get into the chariot,' Dubthach told her.

She jumped up, eyes shining. What a treat to be called away from boring old work.

'Oh I'm so glad to be coming with you. It's such a lovely day!' she chattered excitedly as the heavy chariot rumbled from the house.

Another man might have tried to break the news gently, but Dubthach had never been one to mince his words. Warrior chieftains weren't given to sparing people's feelings.

'I'm taking you to sell you,' he muttered. 'It'll be the king's quern now you'll have to grind.'

Brigid's face fell. She shrank back in her seat, pulling her cloak around her. She'd never had any say in her future. First she'd been taken from her mother…now she was losing the only other family she'd known. All she could do was look to a heavenly Father who had promised never to leave her or forsake her. Silently she prayed until at length the chariot drew to a halt outside the king's fortress.

'Wait here until I get back,' Dubthach instructed as he jumped to the ground. He wanted to do a spot of haggling. After all, if he had to sell the girl, he might as well get a good price for her.

A few moments later he was telling the king of Leinster about the wonderful piece of merchandise waiting outside. She was hardworking … strong … intelligent … resourceful …

'If she's such a catch, why are you so keen to sell her?' the king inquired.

Ah, that was an awkward question. Dubthach cleared his throat. 'I'm selling her because … er … she needs discipline.'

'You mean she's hard to manage?'

'Oh no. Quite the opposite. She's an obedient, good-tempered creature. It's just … well … she sometimes acts first and thinks later. . . .'

'How do you mean?'

'Sometimes – not often, mind – she gives things away.'

Even as this conversation was taking place inside the fortress, outside the fortress a leper was hobbling over to Dubthach's chariot. He was a tall young man, but his whole body had been wrecked by disease. Brigid's soft heart filled with pity at the sight of his deformed hands.

'Help me, help me,' he begged.

What was she to do? As usual she'd nothing of her own to give him – no rings, no gold.

And then her eyes lit on something – a gleaming treasure, inlaid with precious stones.

Without a moment's hesitation the girl handed it over. 'Here, you can have this.'

'Thank you. God bless you.' Eyes wide with delight and astonishment, the leper made off with his prize.

'You did *what*?' Dubthach could hardly believe it when she explained what had happened. As the truth sank in he became almost speechless with rage. 'You…you gave my *sword* to a *leper*? My *sword*! Have you any idea how valuable it was?'

And Brigid's gentle reply only made things worse. 'It was because it was so valuable that I gave it to God,' she kept saying.

In the end all Dubthach could do was drag her before the king. 'She deserves to be whipped … beaten . . .' he raged.

The king of Leinster knit his brows. He was a mighty warrior and had fought many battles over property and wealth. But he had heard enough of the Christian gospel to know that there was another way of looking at things: a way which turned worldly values upside-down – the way of this clear-eyed slave girl.

'Leave her alone,' he said gruffly. 'Her merit before God is greater than ours.'

Dubthach knew when he was beaten. There was no point in trying to sell Brigid. Nor was there any way he could take her home as a slave. So he gave her her freedom. After all, he consoled himself as he set off for home minus one valuable sword, the girl had always belonged to the King of kings. He'd never really owned her anyway.

EXTRA INFORMATION:

St Brigid lived in the second half of the fifth century. There is a shortage of solid historical documentation about her life, and what we know is mainly drawn from legend and folklore. She is portrayed as a woman of great generosity and is said to have founded communities throughout Ireland.

SUGGESTED SONGS:

Behold, what manner of love the Father has given unto us (JP 15)

God is so good (JP 53) (K 78)

Hark, the glad sound! the Saviour comes (JP 68)

I will sing, I will sing a song unto the Lord (JP 126)

O come, O come, Emmanuel (JP 177)

Sing we the King who is coming to reign (JP 218)

Thank You, Lord, for this fine day (JP 232) (CPW 195)

When Israel was in Egypt's land (JP 276)

Everywhere He walks with me (JP 334) (K 48)

Lord, make me a mountain standing tall for You (JP 421)

Educating Alfred

LENGTH: 4–5 minutes. This story works as a mime, requiring two to four people (advisers optional) plus the narrator.

TEACHING POINT: God gives some people the gift of teaching. What sort of learners are we? How do we treat our teachers?

BIBLE READING: Ephesians 4:11; 1 Timothy 5:17–18

In the ninth century well-educated people knew Latin – which meant King Alfred the Great wasn't well-educated. He'd always wanted to learn Latin. But as a boy he'd had no one to teach him, and since then he'd been too busy fighting Vikings to study. Now, at long last, the battles were over, and the king's hunt for a Latin teacher had begun. Because he couldn't find the right man for the job in his own kingdom, he was looking further afield.

'What about Wales? Do we know of any Welsh scholars?' he asked his advisers.

'There's a priest called Asser,' a bishop said thoughtfully. 'I've heard he's an educated man.'

'Ask Asser to come and see me,' commanded the king.

By the end of that meeting Alfred was certain he'd found the perfect teacher. Asser, however, wasn't so sure. Of course it was nice to be noticed and it was good to see his majesty's eagerness to learn. But moving to the English court was a big decision. Asser was a member of a religious community and hated the thought of saying goodbye to people he loved. Therefore he hesitated ... frowning ... stroking his beard ... .

'I'll tell you what. Stay here in England for six months of every year and you can spend the other six back in Wales,' suggested Alfred.

Ah, now this was a much better idea. Six months of every year with his community. The other six here with the king. Asser started to smile. 'Very well. I'll take the job,' he agreed.

So the priest swapped the wilds of Wales for the downs of England, and King Alfred's Latin classes began. Any spare minute he had he would study the Latin Bible with his teacher, translating it line by line. Sometimes Asser would read whole passages aloud and then explain them. 'Copy that out for me,' Alfred would beg him when he found something particularly helpful. And seeing how much the king got out of these exercises, Asser could tell what it was that had kept him calm when the Vikings had been doing their pillaging worst, and what now motivated him to rule his people so wisely and well. King Alfred was a man of faith – a ruler who really wanted to govern God's way.

There was just one problem. Towards the end of November Alfred sent for Asser as usual, but for once the Welshman seemed unwilling to get down to work. 'Your majesty,' he cleared his throat, 'I've been with you now for seven months.'

'Seven months! Have I been learning Latin for seven months already?' The king opened the Bible. 'So how do you think I'm getting on?'

'Your progress is excellent but...'

'*Deus quid fecit caelum et terram*. Seven months ago I wouldn't have understood that. Now I know it means: "God who has made the heaven and earth..."'

'It does indeed but…'

'But what? Did I mispronounce something?'

'Your pronunciation is perfect. It's just that I'm due back in Wales. My brothers are expecting me.'

'Mare et omnia quae in eis sunt,' the king carried on as if he hadn't heard. 'That means "the sea and all things that are in them".'

Asser sighed. It was like setting out to catch an eel in a goblet – getting permission to return home.

The daylight hours grew shorter. Christmas drew near. And still Alfred showed no sign of remembering his side of the bargain. Asser, meanwhile, became more and more resentful. It seemed to him that this king, who was such a great man in so many ways, had one big failing. He took his teacher for granted.

Asser loved teaching. More than that, he believed it was the job God had given him to do. But by Christmas Eve he was ready to toss in the quill.

And then, just after sunset, the king sent for him.

'This is it. I'm going to give his majesty a piece of my mind. He can't go on treating me like this…' The angry scholar strode towards the great hall.

For once he didn't find his royal pupil poring over the Bible. Instead he was on his feet, with his back to the fire, plainly in a holiday mood.

Asser took a deep breath. But before he could open his mouth the king had produced two envelopes from inside his cloak and thrust them into his hands.

'A happy Christmas, my friend,' he said.

'I'm sorry but I refuse…' Asser began.

Again Alfred interrupted him. 'Inside those envelopes you'll find lists of some lands and properties I want you to have,' he smiled. 'It's my way of saying thank you. I'm *very* grateful, you know.'

He winked.

'Make sure you tell those brothers of yours that when you see them.'

'You mean … I can go home?' Asser floundered in a sea of surprise. Here he was all set for a show-down and the king had completely taken the wind from his sails.

'You may go whenever you wish,' Alfred nodded. 'As long as you promise to come back.'

'Of course I'll be back.' There was no longer any question of the king losing his tutor.

A little appreciation had saved the day.

EXTRA INFORMATION:

Alfred the Great, the Saxon King of Wessex, was born in 849 AD and died in 899 AD. After saving England from conquest by the Danes, he built a peaceful society following Christian principles. His interest in books and education led to a great revival of learning and he translated many Latin works into Anglo-Saxon. Asser of Wales remained a close friend and confidant, and eventually wrote his biography.

SUGGESTED SONGS:

Children of Jerusalem (JP 24)

I want to walk with Jesus Christ (JP 124)

Tell me the old, old story (JP 227)

Tell me the stories of Jesus (JP 228)

The best book to read is the Bible (JP 234)

God loves you so much (JP 349) (K 81)

The Grace Cup

LENGTH: 3–4 minutes

TEACHING POINT: God gives us the wisdom we need to influence others.

BIBLE READING: Colossians 4:5–6

At teatime one evening the new queen of Scotland sat at her husband's side in the great hall watching her knights finish their meal. This was the moment when, in Margaret's last court, everyone would have bowed their heads and given thanks for the food. But as usual the Scottish knights forgot. With a clatter of tankards they rose from the table and rushed off to their knightly pursuits.

Sadly the young queen made her own way out of the palace and walked to the nearby church. Margaret loved God, and felt grieved by what she'd just seen. It was hard not to be homesick. Certainly if she'd been given a free choice in the matter she would never have decided to marry the king of Scotland – a man with a fierce temper, almost twice her age. But princesses of royal blood did not have much say in these matters.

Inside the church Margaret knelt at the altar. She took a book – a copy of the four Gospels – from under her cloak and started to read. As always the words strengthened her faith. 'There's no point in self-pity – in moaning about the knights' behaviour or the king's war-like ways,' she told herself. 'God has me here for a purpose.'

She was so taken up with her thoughts she didn't hear King Malcolm's approach.

'Margaret!' She turned round, startled to see his broad frame in the doorway.

'Something upset you.' He came striding towards her down the aisle. 'Don't try to deny it. I saw the look on your face. If one of those knights offended you I ... I'll ...'

'No, Malcolm. It was nothing like that.' Half-laughing, Margaret grabbed hold of his clenched fist. The last thing she wanted to do was send him charging out of the church to throw the knights into jail.

'Well, tell me then.' Suddenly he caught sight of the Gospels sitting on the bench. Ah! The penny dropped. 'You saw something displeasing to God.'

Margaret nodded, touched to see that his eyes which so often blazed with anger were now full of concern. How much should she say? Already her influence over her husband was the talk of the court. Everyone had noticed how eager he had become to find out what the Bible taught. He was a changed man, the knights were saying. But Margaret knew she must be careful. One wrong move could ruin everything.

In the Gospels Jesus told his disciples to trust the Holy Spirit to give them the right words. Now Margaret prayed for wisdom. And even as she prayed she remembered something – a custom she'd seen – and it gave her an idea.

'Malcolm,' she said. 'With your permission there's something I'd like to do after meals...'

In the great hall the following evening there was a sudden lull in the conversation as King Malcolm got to his feet.

'As a mark of her favour, her majesty wishes to send a special cup of wine to every knight who remains behind to give thanks for this meal,' he announced.

There were smiles all round. The knights had got the message – but in the nicest possible way.

At the end of the meal nobody moved. Everyone listened quietly as grace was said. Then the wine, or 'grace drink' as Margaret called it, was passed around the table.

So, as simply as that, without lecturing or causing offence, Queen Margaret persuaded her knights to do the right thing. And watching her the king could see that Christ lived in her heart. And he thanked God for giving him such a wife.

EXTRA INFORMATION:

Margaret was born in 1046 and died in 1093, at the age of forty-seven. She married Malcolm III, king of Scotland, in 1069 and had a great influence upon both church and court. Of her eight children, three became kings of Scotland (Edgar, Alexander and David) while her daughter Matilda married Henry I of England.

SUGGESTED SONGS:

Father, I place into Your hands (JP 42) (CPW 44) (K 457)

Father, lead me day by day (JP 43)

I sing a song of the saints of God (JP 115)

Make me a channel of Your peace (JP 161) (K 248)

Though the world has forsaken God (JP 257)

In everything that I do, show me what Jesus would do (JP 391)

Jesus, send me the helper (JP 409) (K 213)

The Bishop and the King

LENGTH: 5 minutes

TEACHING POINT: Friends, even Christian friends, may let you down in a crisis, but those who trust God never stand alone.

BIBLE READING: 2 Timothy 4:16–18; Mark 14:32–41; Psalm 41

Towards the end of the twelfth century, when Richard the Lionheart ruled England, the bishop of Lincoln was a man called Hugh. Picture an energetic grandfather with twinkling eyes and a very kind face and you'll have some idea what Hugh was like. He was a faithful servant of God and the king – although Richard didn't always appreciate this.

Making war is an expensive business, and on one occasion Richard – who was fighting the French king – came up with a cost-cutting exercise. He asked Hugh to pay for twelve Lincolnshire canons to act as his ambassadors overseas. Now Hugh didn't see why the church should pay clergymen to work for the king. So he said no – whereupon Richard confiscated all Hugh's property.

Panic-stations! The Lincolnshire clergy would have felt the loss of twelve canons, but this was nothing when compared to the loss of their bishop's lands and estates. They decided that Hugh had better lead a delegation to France to sort things out.

The big question was how. Once Hugh and his canons were on French soil nobody seemed quite sure what to do next. The weeks went by. Hugh's canons grew restless. (If you've ever not wanted to go somewhere and had a miserable time when you got there, you'll know how they felt.) Matters came to a head one cold March day when the whole delegation met with the bishop in a draughty French manor. Although no one was openly saying so, there was a certain feeling in the air – the feeling that this was all Hugh's fault.

'We've been here for almost a month,' one canon grumbled. 'And things are getting worse, not better. According to the latest reports, the king has vowed to take revenge on his enemies, and that includes us.'

Revenge. The men shifted fearfully in their seats when they heard that word.

'But we aren't the king's enemies,' Bishop Hugh said mildly. 'I shall make that clear to his majesty when I see him.'

'Make it clear? How will you make it clear?' a second canon demanded.

'Exactly as I've always done. By explaining his duty to God and helping him see where he's gone wrong.'

If the meeting had been a quiz show this would have produced a very loud 'wrong answer' bleep.

'According to the Archbishop of Canterbury, the best way to make it clear we aren't the king's enemies is by sending his majesty a large sum of money,' said Canon Walter Mapp.

Ping! Everyone smiled and nodded.

Hugh felt hurt. Walter was an old friend. Surely he could see this was not the way to act. It was like giving in to terrorism. 'So we buy peace today. But what happens tomorrow? The king wants money like a drowning man wants air. There'll be no end to his demands.'

Nobody nodded this time. Hugh's companions were scared. They didn't want their bishop to stand up to the king. It was too risky. They had too much to lose. Down to a man they urged him to follow Archbishop Hubert's advice and send money.

The discussions went on and on and round and round. By evening Hugh was totally confused. He loved these men as a father. And like any loving parent he found it hard to say no.

'My brothers, this has gone on long enough,' he said at last. 'Let's ask God to guide us to the best decision. We'll meet again in the morning.'

The hall emptied in silence. And Hugh, now utterly alone, went to spend long hours on his knees, begging God to show him what to do.

Finally he went to bed. To begin with he tossed and turned. And then the dream came – a wonderfully encouraging dream. 'God will give strength and power to his people,' a heavenly voice promised.

The twinkle was back in Hugh's eyes when he got up next morning. He had his answer. It wouldn't have mattered if every clergyman in Europe had tried to talk him out of it. He would send no money to the king.

Funnily enough the canons did not come back that day, nor the next. Instead, a short time later, Hugh had a visit from his old friend the Abbess Matilde. One look at her face was enough to tell him that this was no passing call. Something had happened. It was being hushed up for the time being. But because of the huge difference it would make to Hugh's situation, she thought he should know. King Richard was on his deathbed. He wouldn't be taking revenge on anyone now.

A less saintly man than Hugh would probably have been very glad to hear it. But Hugh, being Hugh, was genuinely upset. In fact the only thing that brought him any comfort was the news that in his final illness the king had turned to God. And some words of Richard's (somewhat modernised here!) showed that underneath it all the king respected Hugh and saw him as a friend. 'If all church leaders were like Hugh,' he'd said, 'there's not a king in Christendom would dare say boo to a bishop.'

EXTRA INFORMATION:

Saint Hugh of Lincoln was born around 1140 in Avalon, France, and died in London on 16th November 1200. Before becoming Bishop of Lincoln in 1186, he served as the first prior of the Carthusian house at Witham, in Somerset. Both as prior and as bishop Hugh consistently defended the church's liberties. At the same time his holiness and sincerity won him the respect of the three English kings under whom he served – King Henry II, King Richard I and King John.

SUGGESTED SONGS:

Be bold, Be strong (JP 14) (CPW 11) (K 17)

Glory to You, my God, this night (JP 52)

God is our guide, our light and our deliverer (JP 56)

How great is our God! How great is His name! (JP 82)

I sing a song of the saints of God (JP 115)

Thank You for ev'ry new good morning (JP 230)

What a friend we have in Jesus (JP 273) (CPW 228)

Spies were sent out to (JP 464)

Friar Bacon Experiments

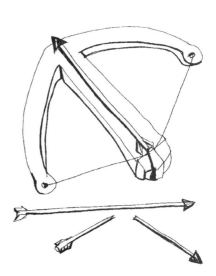

LENGTH: 4–5 minutes

TEACHING POINT: The proof of our love for God should be seen in our actions.

BIBLE READING: 1 John 2:1–6

The Franciscan scholar Roger Bacon is sometimes seen as the herald of modern science. He certainly believed in the value of experiments – and not just of the chemical kind. The story goes that once, when Bacon was out for his morning walk, he noticed a bit of a fuss on the village green. At first he put it down to the king and his royal court being in town. Then he saw the three young men and the flash of steel plate in the sun.

The bystanders cheerfully put him in the picture.

'Those three are brothers,' a washerwoman explained. 'Their father died last week. The trouble is that instead of choosing an heir in the normal way, the old man left his property to the son who loved him best. And now each brother is claiming to be the most loving.'

'It's a tricky one,' a merchant agreed. 'I mean, who's to judge? The lawyers haven't been able to settle things. The brothers refuse to divide the land up. So the king has granted them permission to fight to the death.' He rubbed his hands gleefully as the tallest young man snapped down the pig-faced visor on his helmet. 'The two eldest will fight. Then the winner of the first fight will fight the youngest. And the winner of *that* fight will get the land.'

Bacon frowned. He didn't like to think of three fine young men killing each other over an inheritance.

Quickly the friar made his way to King Edward's tent. 'Sire,' he bowed deeply. 'I've just been told what's going on and now I beg you to stop the fight. I believe the matter may be settled without bloodshed.'

Another monarch might have resented such meddling. But King Edward welcomed the chance to save the young men. 'I'm content to leave the matter in your hands,' he nodded graciously. Then he stopped the duel and had the brothers brought before him.

They didn't quite know whether to be relieved or disappointed when they heard about Bacon's offer.

'Will you accept his judgement?' King Edward asked.

The brothers looked at each other grumpily. Yes, they would accept the friar's decision, they shrugged. They couldn't help wondering how he would make it, though. Surely no one – not even the cleverest man in Europe – could measure the amount of love in a human heart?

'Go home for now,' Bacon told them. 'It will be three days before I can deliver my verdict.'

So the young men went home and the friar laid his plans. 'You could call it a sort of human experiment,' he told the king.

He was waiting for the brothers, weighed down under three crossbows and a quiver of arrows, when they returned three days later. What was going on? Were they to fight after all? Surprised and puzzled, the young men followed him into a secluded spot among the trees.

There Bacon laid the weapons out on the ground. 'As you know, this is a very difficult matter,' he said gravely. 'And there is no way we can solve it pleasantly. It was your father who got you into this mess and he must get you out of it.'

The young men looked more puzzled than ever. How could a dead man get anyone out of anything?

'With the king's permission I have had his body taken from the grave,' the friar continued. 'It is now behind a screen on the village green, propped up against a post. What I have planned is this. The three of you will go onto the green and there, in the presence of the king and his stewards, treasurers, clerks and chaplains, you will each shoot a single arrow. The son whose arrow lands closest to your father's heart will inherit his property.'

There was a moment or two of silence while the friar's words sank in. 'Well, let's get on with it,' the eldest son said as he bent down to lift his weapon.

'You got first pick of the bows. I get first shot,' the second son retorted as he elbowed him out of the way.

The youngest son didn't move. 'Here. Take your weapon.' Bacon held out the remaining bow.

Suddenly the young man burst into tears. 'You ought to be ashamed of yourselves,' he shouted at his brothers. 'How can you possibly allow our father to be used like this? I'd rather lose everything than wound the body I so loved when it was alive.'

No sooner were the words out of his mouth than Friar Bacon placed a comforting hand upon his shoulder. His human experiment had worked. All three men had insisted they loved their father, but only one had acted in a loving way.

'The contest is over. The property goes to this youngest son,' the wise friar said.

EXTRA INFORMATION:

Roger Bacon was born around 1220 and died around 1292. The above story is one of a number of popular legends told about him. Whether or not the actual events ever took place, they have some basis in reality. Bacon was a man of immense learning and a major medieval proponent of experimental science.

SUGGESTED SONGS:

God's not dead (No) (JP 60) (CPW 66) (K 85)

God whose Son was once a man on earth (JP 62)

In our work and in our play (JP 108)

Keep me shining, Lord (JP 147)

May the mind of Christ my Saviour (JP 165)

A new commandment that I give to you (JP 303) (CPW 3)

It's the little things that show our love for Jesus (JP 403)

Family Values

LENGTH: 5 minutes

TEACHING POINT: The importance of forgiveness in family and church life.

BIBLE READING: Ephesians 4:25–32

In the Middle Ages girls married young. Bridget was only thirteen when she and Ulf Gudmarsson tied the knot. She was barely seventeen when her first child, Marta, was born. And by the time she hit thirty, Ulf had begun looking round for a suitable husband for Marta.

Now Ulf was an important man in fourteenth-century Sweden. And being an important man, he often rubbed shoulders with other important men. And one day he rubbed shoulders with a certain Sir Sigvid Ribbing. Hmm. Ulf eyed him thoughtfully. Sir Sigvid was a fine-looking chap. Not only that, he had money, *and* he was connected with royalty. Hmm … hmm … (Can you guess what Ulf was thinking?)

It wasn't too long after that that the big news broke.

Prepare for a wedding.

There were smiles and congratulations all round. The bride's father was delighted. The bride-to-be was delighted. The bridegroom was delighted. The bride's six brothers and sisters were delighted. The only person who wasn't delighted was the bride's mother, Bridget.

Bridget didn't want Sir Sigvid Ribbing as a son-in-law – no, not if he was the last man on earth. While Ulf looked at Sir Sigvid's high position and liked what he saw, Bridget looked at his character. Sir Sigvid was important, certainly, but he was also cruel. Yes, he was wealthy, but at whose expense? Sir Sigvid *Robbing* would have been a better name for him. In Bridget's eyes he was the worst kind of thief – the kind who demanded unfair taxes from the poor.

'You *can't* give Marta to that scoundrel. I won't allow it,' she told Ulf.

Now Ulf had got himself into a tight corner. He loved his wife. And he respected her views. In fifteen years of married life they'd hardly ever had a minor disagreement, never mind a major quarrel. He could see he might have been a little hasty in promising Marta to Sigvid, but he couldn't go back on his word to such an important person. It was *unthinkable*.

Bridget's face went chalk white when he explained this. 'In that case,' she said stiffly, 'I shall have nothing to do with the wedding.'

Nothing to do with the wedding! Now it was Ulf's turn to go white. What were Sir Sigvid Ribbing and all his important friends and relatives going to think when the bride's mother didn't receive them into her home? At first he shrugged his shoulders and hoped that Bridget would come round. But she didn't. Not only did this make preparations difficult (Ulf had to see to the feast and order the flowers!), it was bad for Bridget's health. Bridget was expecting a baby – their eighth. And by the looks of things it would be arriving into a very unhappy home.

The wedding day came. And Bridget remained in her room. Ulf begged her to come down. He reasoned. He threatened. But in the end, he had to go and welcome the guests alone.

Bridget, for her part, was the angriest she'd ever been in her life. Now there are different kinds of anger. There's a wrong, selfish anger – the sort we feel when we don't get our own way. And then there's a right, unselfish anger – the sort we feel when we see God's law being broken and other people being hurt. It was that second kind of anger which had taken hold of Bridget. Here was a woman who really loved God. And here was her own husband handing their daughter over to an evil man.

Bridget was so upset she felt sure her heart would break. In fact she almost wished it would. 'Lord, I cannot bear this!' She threw herself to her knees. And then, suddenly, beneath the pound … pound … pound … of her own heart she felt the tap … tap … tap … of her unborn child. And she heard God speaking to her through the voice of this child saying: 'Mother, Mother, do not kill me. For if you die now, I'll die too! And I really want to live.'

At this Bridget got up. She stood for a moment, listening to the sound of music and laughter downstairs. Then she pulled on a fine embroidered dress and went down to the great hall. Without a word she made her way over to Ulf. She slipped her hand into his and took her place by his side.

'I still don't agree with you,' her actions said. 'But there are other things, besides Marta's future, to think of. There's our marriage and our new baby. For their sake, I'm willing to let my anger go.'

A few days later the couple's daughter Cecilia was born – a sturdy little girl who grew up to live a long, rewarding life. While she was still a toddler, Bridget and Ulf made pilgrimages together, and Ulf became more committed to God. As for Marta, well, just as Bridget had feared, her marriage *was* unhappy. Sir Sigvid didn't live long, though, and the couple's son Peter turned out really well. So even in the bad there was good. God worked things out. And Bridget went on to help many people through her writings and ministry – a ministry for which she is remembered to this day.

EXTRA INFORMATION:

Bridget of Sweden was born around 1303 and died in 1373. She had eight children: Marta, Karl, Birger, Bengt, Gudmar, Karin, Ingeborg and Cecilia. After her husband's death in 1343 she came to prominence as a Christian mystic and played an influencial role in national affairs. She founded the Brigittine Order of Sisters and is the patron saint of Sweden.

SUGGESTED SONGS:

Bind us together, Lord (JP 17) (CPW 18)

Dear Lord and Father of mankind (JP 37)

For the beauty of the earth (JP 48)

Now the green blade riseth (JP 174)

Lord we ask now to receive Your blessing (JP 301)

A naggy mum, a grumpy dad, a brother who's a pain (JP 302)

Saul had made himself a number of enemies (JP 450)

Thank You for the love that our mums give to us each day (JP 467)

Tax Free!

LENGTH: 5–6 minutes. This story will work as a mime. As well as the narrator you will need someone with the skill to convey Jack's feeling through body language and facial expression. (The herald and members of the crowd are optional.)

TEACHING POINT: In the Bible the word 'debts' is often used to refer to human 'sins'. God frees us from our debts because of what Jesus has done.

BIBLE READING: Matthew 6:12; Matthew 18:23–27; Hebrews 10:11–14

Allow me to introduce you to a fifteenth-century French peasant farmer. His name is Jack and he's a man of substance. Jack is no down-trodden peasant, you understand. He's an important man in his village – with public duties and an official title. The title – *douanier* – is hard to pronounce so let's forget it. All we need to remember is what his public duties involve. Jack organises the night watch, guards prisoners and collects taxes. Got that?

Anyway, at the time when we meet up with him, Jack isn't doing any of those things. No. For once in his life work is the last thing on his mind. For the past two weeks Jack has been on holiday in the city of Rheims, staying with his wife in the Striped Donkey Inn opposite the cathedral. And to the landlady's delight he's showing no signs of going home.

So why is a normally hardworking peasant farmer frittering away precious time? Answer – our Jack is celebrating.

Next question. What has Jack got to celebrate? OK, this is a bit complicated, so listen carefully. In the fifteenth century the English laid claim to the French throne. Henry VI was their man for the job, and for a while they had the French on the run. Then, out of the blue, a French peasant girl appeared, claiming God had sent her to drive the English out of France. Next minute the French were making a comeback, lifting sieges and sweeping all before them until on 17th July 1429 their man – Charles VII – was crowned in Rheims Cathedral. And this is where Jack comes in. The peasant girl responsible for the whole amazing operation was none other than his seventeen-year-old daughter Joan.

Our Jack is celebrating the fact that he's the father of a national heroine. Everywhere he goes he hears people talking about his daughter. And when they find out who *he* is, well, they're practically queuing for his autograph. 'What was the maid like as a child?' they ask. 'When did she first begin to feel that God was calling her to save France?'

Now Jack doesn't mind talking to the fifteenth-century press. (We call them 'press' in the sense that they're a lot of people all pressing in on Jack.) He's happy to tell them that Joan had always been an ordinary girl. Healthy. Hardworking. Yes, she'd always been very devout, and sometimes slipped into the church alone to pray.

At the same time there are some questions he tries to avoid. He prefers not to say how furious he was when she first spoke of her mission. He can't remember whether he actually boxed her ears then, or whether he's confusing that occasion with the time she'd refused to marry the husband he'd chosen for her. Either way, it's embarrassing. He doesn't want to go down in history as the man who'd almost stopped the maid from saving France. So he avoids awkward questions and thanks God that Joan was sure enough of her calling not to let him stand in her way.

All in all Jack is having the time of his life. There's just one cloud on his horizon. It's the sort of worry you're bound to have when a close friend or relative shoots to fame. You wonder whether success has changed them. You ask yourself if they've forgotten their roots. Poor Jack only sees his daughter from a distance these days. And the glittering figure on horseback seems a hundred light years away from the simple girl in a red woollen dress who lived under his roof for seventeen years. What's going on in her mind? he wonders. Does she ever think of her family and friends?

Now people didn't send postcards in those days. But Joan sends her dad the next best thing. It comes in the shape of the king's herald. You know what a herald is? Someone who blows a trumpet and makes official announcements in a foghorn voice. Anyway this herald rides into the market place. He toots on his trumpet. 'Hear ye … hear ye . . .' he begins. And then, when he has everyone's attention, he tells them, in the usual flowery way, what the king has just decided.

'In honour of, and at the request of, our beloved Joan the Maid, in consideration of the great, high, noteworthy and profitable service she has done us, and does each day for the recovery of our sovereignty, we hereby decree that the villages of Domremy and Greux be released from all taxes in perpetuity,' he bawls.

Of course it takes Jack a minute or two to translate this into plain French. But what it actually boils down to is this: his daughter has asked that the people of her village shouldn't pay any more taxes – ever! And Charles VII has agreed!

Well, a little while after this, our Jack's summer holiday comes to an end. He goes home to Domremy. He continues to farm his land. As village overseer, he carries on with his public duties. What did we say they were? Organising the night watch, guarding prisoners, collecting taxes. Hey, wait a minute! When the time comes to gather taxes things are different. Jack can sit back. There's no more badgering villagers who can't pay, no more adding up columns of figures. Thanks to the king's decree, he's only the briefest entry to make in his account book. One word sums up how much is owed, two words give the reason. Against the name of Domremy he writes, 'Nothing – the maid.'

106   50 Five-Minute Stories

EXTRA INFORMATION:

Joan of Arc (Jeanne D'Arc) was born in 1412. In 1429 her military and political intervention altered the course of the war, although it was many more years before the English were finally driven out of France. Joan herself was captured in battle, and burnt at the stake as a heretic in 1431. A later court in 1456 found her innocent. The villages of Domremy and Greux continued to enjoy tax-free status for over 300 years, until the time of the French Revolution.

SUGGESTED SONGS:

God is so good (JP 53) (K 78)

God sent His Son, they call Him Jesus (JP 58)

He paid a debt He did not owe (JP 77)

Jesus Christ is risen today, Hallelujah! (JP 130)

Jesus is Lord! Creation's voice proclaims it (JP 137)

To God be the glory! Great things He has done! (JP 259)

Teamwork

LENGTH: 4–5 minutes

TEACHING POINT: God's kingdom is not built up through solo performances, but through working together with Christ.

BIBLE READING: 1 Corinthians 3:1–11; 2 Chronicles 2:1–18

This is the story of a sculpture – a sculpture showing three people grouped round the body of Christ. On the right is the Virgin Mary. On the left is Mary Magdalene. At the back the hooded figure with the kind, sad face is Nicodemus. The whole work speaks of the love these followers had for their Lord. But it has another message – a secret message hidden in its past.

The sculpture began life way back in Roman times as a marble block sitting at the top of a column, supporting a Roman temple. Eventually the temple fell down and the block came into the possession of one of the greatest artists ever known – a man called Michelangelo.

He set to work. Chip … chip … chip. The marble was hard and full of flaws but gradually as the old man chipped and chiselled the figures began to emerge – a masterpiece in the making.

And then one day disaster struck. Maybe the same sort of thing has happened to you. There you are painting or drawing away when – whoops – the pen or the paintbrush slips and you're left with an ugly great blot on the page. In this case it was the chisel that slipped. Oh no! Michelangelo stood back to discover he'd chipped too much marble from Mary's elbow.

We won't ask what you'd do in that sort of situation. But here's what Michelangelo did. He lost his temper. He turned round and roared at his servant. 'Now look what's happened. It's all *your* fault. You're always bothering me!' Then he turned back to his sculpture. 'It's ruined! Ruined!' Seeing no way of fixing the elbow, he lifted his hammer and chisel and began to knock great chunks out of the figures, just the way you might tear up a spoilt painting.

His servants Urbino and Antonio looked on in horror. Clunk. A chunk of marble fell on the floor. Was it Nicodemus's nose? Or Mary's eyebrow?

'Stop! Please!' Antonio sprang forward. 'Don't break up the sculpture. Give it to me.'

'Take it then.' Michelangelo threw down the hammer and chisel.

So the damaged sculpture was handed over to Antonio.

For years the servant kept it in his room. He often looked at it, and dusted it occasionally, but that was as much as he could do.

And then, when Michelangelo was well into his eighties, he took on a young apprentice called Tiberio. In some ways Tiberio was a bit like a loveable puppy – full of enthusiasm. He was full of curiosity too, and one day he happened to notice the broken pieces from the sculpture lying in the cellar. 'Where did those come from?' he inquired.

By the time Antonio had finished explaining, Tiberio was beside himself with excitement.

'An unfinished sculpture! Brilliant!' he cried. 'Where is it?'

'Where do you think?' said Antonio. 'Michelangelo gave it to me. It's in my room.'

'Let me have it,' Tiberio begged. 'I'll try to restore it.'

Hmm. Antonio looked doubtful. The sculpture was his and he liked having it around.

'I'll give you something in return,' Tiberio promised. 'After all, you know you can't do anything with it yourself.'

There was no denying that. Antonio had saved the sculpture, but he couldn't fix it!

'All right then. See what you can do,' Antonio agreed.

So Tiberio took the sculpture to his workplace. Months passed – months during which the young apprentice chipped away from dawn to dusk, often turning to Michelangelo for advice. Patiently he restored the figures of Nicodemus and the Virgin Mary. Skilfully he chiselled out the figure of Mary Magdalene. Faithfully he captured the spirit of love. And finally the whole thing was complete.

The end result of Tiberio's enthusiasm, Antonio's care and Michelangelo's genius may be seen today in the cathedral in Florence. No doubt many of the visitors who stop to admire it are unaware of its history. But there the sculpture stands – an artistic masterpiece, with a message about teamwork hidden in its past.

EXTRA INFORMATION:

Michelangelo, one of the greatest artists of the Renaissance, was born in 1475 and died in 1564. His finest sculptures include the Pieta (1499) in the Vatican, David (1504) at Florence and Moses (1545) also in the Vatican. In the sculpture referred to in the above story Michelangelo's hooded Nicodemus is said to be an idealised self-portrait.

SUGGESTED SONGS:

For I'm building a people of power (JP 47) (CPW 48) (K 61)

Let us praise God together (JP 152)

Our eyes have seen the glory of our Saviour, Christ the Lord (JP 191)

We really want to thank You, Lord (JP 268)

I am the Church! (JP 367)

Kids under construction (JP 414)

Maybe you can't draw or sing or be a football star (JP 429)

A Question of Survival

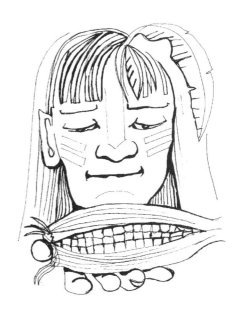

LENGTH: 4–5 minutes

TEACHING POINT: Through Jesus we may experience friendship with God and the Holy Spirit's guidance and help.

BIBLE READING: John 4:6–26; Isaiah 65:17–25

In the seventeenth century a certain William Brewster gave his children rather unusual names. He called one son Love and another Wrestling. In Wrestling's case it wasn't the physical kind of wrestling William had in mind. It was the spiritual wrestling you did with the forces of evil, and with kings and religious authorities out to stop you worshipping God the way you felt you should.

The Brewster family were Separatists, which meant that on Sundays, instead of going to their local church, they held their own services; one in the morning from around eight until midday, and another from two o'clock until teatime! Now whatever you think of four-hour services, you'd probably agree that people should be free to attend them if they wish. But in seventeenth-century England Separatists were given a very hard time. They were insulted, informed on, fired from their jobs and sometimes imprisoned – with the result that a number of them decided to live somewhere else. They went to Holland first. But within a few years they were planning to move on … right across the Atlantic Ocean to the New World of North America.

And so on 20th September 1620 William Brewster, his wife Mary, nine-year-old Love and six-year-old Wrestling set sail.

The voyage was a nightmare. For sixty-seven days their ship, *The Mayflower*, bobbed like a cork on the angry ocean, lashed by the wind and waves. On board conditions were appalling – 120 cold, wet, smelly, seasick people all crowded into a space the size of a tennis court.

You can imagine their relief when they finally reached land. That Monday, for the first time in six and a half weeks, Love and Wrestling got a chance to stretch their legs. With the wind in their hair and the ground of the New World firm under their feet they may have felt the worst hardships were over. But they were wrong.

The pilgrims (as they've become known) had landed in a northerly spot at a miserable time of year. Already winter had set in. The landscape was bleak and windswept. They were weak and exhausted. With typical grit they got down to the huge task of building a whole town from scratch. But it was too much. Before long men, women and children were dying like flies – sometimes as many as three in one day. As if that wasn't bad enough, their bodies had to be buried in flat graves at the dead of night. Why? Because the pilgrims believed that if the local Indians discovered how few able-bodied men were left to defend the settlement, they would attack and wipe everyone out.

For four gruelling months the settlers clung to life by the fingertips. And then, as the first buds of spring began to change the wintry landscape, their fortunes began to change too.

First came a meeting with the local Indian chief. Chief Massasoit was his name, and his face was painted a tasteful shade of mulberry the day he appeared on a small hill facing the settlement. He'd brought sixty red, white, yellow and black painted Indian braves with him. But fortunately it was a friendly visit. With great ceremony the chief allowed himself to be escorted into a pilgrim cottage. There, seated on a green rug, he and the settlers drew up an agreement. *They* promised, among other things, that they wouldn't steal from the Indians. Chief Massasoit promised that the Indians would let them settle in peace.

But there was more. When Massasoit and his braves finally took their leave, they left someone behind: an Indian called Squanto. Squanto had been to London. He could speak good English. And he had stayed behind to act as the pilgrims' guide. It was Squanto who taught them the secrets of the soil. Thanks to him that year they had a harvest to gather in, and a harvest celebration to which they invited their Indian friends.

So the pilgrims survived. Their colony flourished. And today all over North America people celebrate their achievement. But their story raises a question. Those settlers survived because, knowing they couldn't go it alone, they were ready to accept Chief Massasoit's friendship and Squanto's guidance. The question is: Are we as ready as they were to accept help? Today, through Jesus, God offers *us* the gift of friendship. We can receive his Holy Spirit as our guide. Now – as then – it's a question of survival. Us surviving death to enjoy perfect freedom in God's new world.

Think about it. OK?

EXTRA INFORMATION:

The pilgrims landed in what is now Massachusetts and established a settlement they called Plymouth. Not all the passengers on board *The Mayflower* were Separatists. A number were simply people of modest means hoping to make a better life for themselves in the New World. Wrestling Brewster died in 1635 and Love in 1650. Today families in North America remember the settlers' first harvest thanksgiving feast on Thanksgiving Day – a national holiday celebrated on the last Thursday in November.

SUGGESTED SONGS:

Come, you thankful people, come (JP 32)

God is our guide, our light and our deliverer (JP 56)

Have you heard the raindrops drumming on the rooftops? (JP 71) (K 99)

He who would valiant be (JP 80) (CPW 82)

I'm feeding on the living bread (JP 104)

My faith is like a staff of oak (JP 168)

One more step along the world I go (JP 188) (CPW 169) (K 273)

Our harvest day is over for yet another year (JP 193)

Will your anchor hold in the storms of life (JP 290)

It takes an almighty hand to make your harvest grow (JP 395) (K 176)

Deceived!

LENGTH: 6 minutes. This story will work as a mime. It requires five people plus the narrator. (The person miming Cagliostro may double as the hoax queen.)

TEACHING POINT: The Bible tells us who we should listen to – and who we shouldn't!

BIBLE READING: Matthew 17:1–5; 2 Peter 2:1–3

Louis Rene Edward Rohan – we'll call him Ron – was an eighteenth-century French cardinal. Like most of the Frenchmen of his day he strutted around wearing tights, a powdered wig and a courtly smile. But when we first meet him, Cardinal Ron isn't smiling. He's got a problem. He can't get Queen Marie Antoinette to speak to him, no matter what he does or how hard he tries.

Now let's be clear about this. Ron's reasons for wanting to get into the queen's good books are selfish. Our Ron is ambitious. And he knows he'll never get anywhere without the queen's support.

One person who does support Ron is his friend Cagliostro – an unusual man to put it mildly. Cagliostro claims to have been alive during the time of the pharaohs and describes himself as a prophet. (He's got a beard to prove it!) Other people might describe him as two chimpanzees short of a tea-party. But after a session with Cagliostro, our Ron's smile is always firmly glued back in position. Cagliostro never fails to predict that Ron is on his way to the top.

And one day Ron has a surprising visitor. She's a woman called Jeanne and she claims to be best friends with the queen. 'Me and Marie Antoinette are like that!' She puts her fingers one on top of the other, to show how close they are. 'If you like I'll try and interest her in your career.'

If you like! Ron doesn't just like the idea, he *loves* it.

A few days later Jeanne is back with some encouraging news. 'I've talked to the queen,' she says. 'Watch closely at the next court function. She'll nod towards you as a sign of her goodwill.'

At the next court function Ron watches the queen like a hawk. Now if you'd been standing beside Ron at that function you probably wouldn't have noticed a thing. But, buoyed up by Cagliostro's prophecies, Ron is sure he detects a significant dip of the royal head.

After that there seems to be no limit to what Jeanne can achieve. First she persuades Marie Antoinette to write to Ron – gracious letters on gilt-edged paper embossed with the royal emblem. Then she persuades the queen to meet Ron and give him a rose. The meeting takes place on a dark, moonless August night in a leafy grove in the palace grounds. If you'd been with Ron at that meeting you might have wondered why the queen was wearing such a thick veil, and why Jeanne rushed him away so quickly. But, buoyed up by Cagliostro's prophecies, Ron looks at the rose and sees it as the promise of great things to come.

What comes next is a *very special* request. Jeanne persuades the queen to ask Ron to help her buy the most expensive piece of jewellery in France: a diamond necklace costing well over a million pounds. All he has to do is collect it from the jeweller and deliver it to her via her dear friend Jeanne.

Now if you'd been involved in delivering that necklace you might have asked a few questions – like how could you be sure that Jeanne really *would* pass it on to the queen. But Ron isn't suspicious. Not with Cagliostro's prophecies ringing in his ears. He does exactly what Jeanne tells him: draws up a contract with the jeweller, collects the necklace and brings it to her lodgings in Versailles.

And a few months later it looks as if all his efforts are about to be rewarded. King Louis sends for him.

'I wonder what it's about?' Ron rubs his chin and waits expectantly while Cagliostro peers into his crystal ball.

'You are destined for greatness, my friend. Soon you will hold the highest office in the land.'

Ron is like the cat that got the cream as he sets out for Versailles. 'Make way for the future prime minister,' he thinks as he steps out of his carriage and sweeps through the hall of mirrors. There's just time to check his wig is on straight and his tights aren't wrinkled before he's shown into the king's study.

And there sits the king with Queen Marie Antoinette by his side.

But something is wrong. This queen, whom he has served so well, looks angry and upset.

'Can you explain this?' Coldly King Louis throws a letter across the table.

Ron reads it but doesn't see anything to explain. It's a letter from the jeweller. 'Dear King,' it says. 'This is just to remind you that I still haven't been paid for the necklace collected by Cardinal Louis Rene Edward Rohan on behalf of the queen.'

So? Ron raises his eyebrows. He delivered the necklace. If the king and queen haven't paid for it yet that's *their* problem, not his.

'Her majesty did not receive any necklace,' declares the king. 'Nor did she ever wish to buy it.'

'But ... but ... I brought it to Jeanne de la Motte's lodgings here in Versailles.' Ron looks stunned.

Now you probably saw that coming. In fact if you'd been around to advise Ron, you'd have been able to save him a great deal of embarrassment. And then again, you might not. For the trouble with Ron is that he's a habit of listening to the wrong voices: Cagliostro's voice, Jeanne's voice, the voice of his own ambition.

And now he has to listen to the king's voice coldly and clearly repeating the harsh facts. Queen Marie Antoinette hasn't got the necklace. And she doesn't want it either.

Poor old Ron! The bottom has just fallen out of his imaginary world.

For the first time in months he sees clearly. The diamonds didn't go to the queen, they went to Jeanne. The letters were forged. The midnight meeting was a hoax. Cagliostro's prophecies were nonsense.

He's been deceived!

EXTRA INFORMATION:

Louis Rene Edouard Rohan was born in 1734. After the necklace affair he stood trial for fraud and had to use all his powers of intelligence to prove he'd been taken in by Jeanne. He narrowly escaped the guillotine during the French Revolution.

SUGGESTED SONGS:

Don't build your house on the sandy land (JP 39) (CPW 38) (K 40)

I met Jesus at the crossroads (JP 102)

My Lord is higher than a mountain (JP 170)

The wise man built his house upon the rock (JP 252) (CPW 205) (K 336)

Turn your eyes upon Jesus (JP 260)

What Betsy Did

LENGTH: 4 minutes

TEACHING POINT: Through faith we can do great things for God.

BIBLE READING: Hebrews 11:23–40

In the nineteenth century keeping a diary or journal was a popular thing to do. Betsy Gurney was just a girl when she began writing in her secret little book. At first she did it out of duty, but before long it became a pleasure. Her diary never disapproved of anything she said. It never asked awkward questions. She could tell it things she kept hidden from everyone else. It heard how she longed to *do* something in life; how she was afraid of the dark. And the sea. And of dying. It knew how night after night she had the same horrible dream of being washed out to sea to struggle until she drowned.

Then one February Betsy met a travelling preacher called William. They talked, and for the very first time she sensed God's love. 'I have *felt* there is a God,' she wrote in her diary. That night she dreamed as usual that the sea was coming to carry her away. But this time the dream ended differently. Instead of being swept out into the ocean to struggle and drown, she was held safe – beyond reach of the waves.

The big question next morning was whether this new-found peace would last. She didn't have much time to spend with her diary over the next two months because her father took her to London. (He'd noticed she'd seemed rather out of sorts and thought a taste of city life might cheer her up.) London *was* exciting and Betsy thoroughly enjoyed her stay. But she had something much more important to write about when she returned home. In the two months since she'd first talked with William she hadn't had any more nightmares. God had stopped them. 'It ought, I think, to make my faith steady,' she wrote.

Years later Betsy (now known as Elizabeth) was back in London, as the wife of a Mr Joseph Fry and the busy mother of ten children. Not only had her faith remained steady but somehow she still found time to write her diary. 'I have lately been much occupied in forming a school in Newgate for the children of poor prisoners,' she noted in 1817.

What a story lay behind those words!

That January Elizabeth had left the warmth of her home and the chatter of her children to visit some of the most miserable people in the whole city: the women prisoners who, along with their small children, lived under the most dreadful conditions in Newgate jail.

The turnkeys thought she was mad, especially when she insisted she wanted to go in to the women alone. Couldn't she hear the racket? Animals behaved better than those women. They spent their time drinking and fighting. Why, the prison governor himself wouldn't go through that gate unguarded.

Their arguments had no effect. Elizabeth insisted on going into the yard. She wouldn't even leave her gold watch behind for safe-keeping.

Inside the gates the prisoners crowded round her. Staring. Jostling. Pulling at her dress. What would happen next? 'We tried to warn her,' the turnkeys muttered as they shook their heads.

One wrong move and things could easily have turned nasty. But God showed Elizabeth exactly what to do. At the front of the crowd there were a number of dirty, ragged children. She simply lifted the smallest one and held it in her arms. 'Is there not something we can do for these little ones?' she asked. 'Do you want them to grow up to be prisoners themselves?'

The pushing and jostling stopped. Before the turnkeys' astonished eyes, the wild women proved that they were human after all. Of course they wanted something better for their children. And so for the next few hours Elizabeth Fry and the women talked. She told them about Jesus. She read to them from the Bible. And together they laid plans for a prison school where the children could learn to read and write.

That school was a turning point – the first of many reforms to prison conditions. 'A remarkable blessing appears to accompany my prison concerns,' Elizabeth later wrote in her diary.

The girl who had battled with fear had accomplished great things.

So much can happen when God takes control of our lives.

EXTRA INFORMATION:

Elizabeth Fry was born in 1780 and died in 1845. Her father was a Quaker banker from Norwich, and she married a strict Quaker. Elizabeth herself became a 'minister' of the Society of Friends. She travelled widely to further her prison work and her reforming efforts bore fruit both at home and abroad.

SUGGESTED SONGS:

Be bold, Be strong (JP 14) (CPW 11) (K 17)

Father, I place into Your hands (JP 42) (CPW 44) (K 457)

God's not dead (No) (JP 60) (CPW 66) (K 85)

I am a lighthouse, a shining and bright house (JP 87) (K 114)

My God is so big (JP 169) (CPW 157) (K 255)

Now be strong and very courageous (JP 172)

Will your anchor hold in the storms of life (JP 290)

No Fleas!
No Bugs!

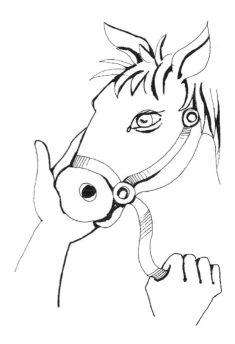

LENGTH: 7–8 minutes

TEACHING POINT: God went to great lengths to bring about our salvation. To what lengths will we go to share that good news?

BIBLE READING: Luke 14:16–24

Gladys Aylward and Jeannie Lawson were two small women keen to do big things for God. Jeannie had been a missionary in China for over fifty years, while her young companion had just travelled thousands of miles by train, boat, bus and mule to join her. They were living together in a large delapidated house in the walled city of Yangcheng.

They'd come to Yangcheng to tell people about Jesus. The trouble was the Chinese peasants who farmed this lonely mountainous spot had never seen Westerners before. Jeannie's white hair terrified them, and so did Gladys's pale skin. When the pair ventured out into the narrow city streets, women would slam their doors and spit. Men threw mud. Children followed them, pointing and shouting insults. Nobody wanted to have anything to do with the 'foreign devils'.

Although the city was so isolated, it was a very busy place. Every afternoon hundreds of traders would file in through the East Gate to stop overnight, before journeying on next morning. They came with their mules, and were often accompanied by teams of human carriers, balancing heavy bundles on either end of long poles.

'If only we could tell those men the good news, they could carry it for hundreds of miles through the province,' Gladys said to Jeannie one day.

Since the muleteers and carriers were as hostile as the local peasants, this was nothing more than a wistful remark. But Jeannie leapt on it, like a dog on a bone.

'The traders! Of course! That's the answer!' Excitedly she shook Gladys's arm. 'We'll open an inn.'

'Open an inn?' Gladys wondered if she'd heard correctly. Hundreds of inns were to be found along the narrow streets of Yangcheng, each offering the same deal to weary travellers. For two cash (the equivalent of a couple of pence) they got a meal and a place on the communal brick bed under which hot air flowed from the stove.

'I can't imagine why I didn't think of it sooner!' Eagerly Jeannie surveyed the downstairs room of the house. 'This place was built as an inn. Look at that!' She pointed to the brick bed. 'That *k'ang* runs the entire length of the wall. All we need to do is get the roof mended, stick up a sign and we could easily take in fifty travellers a night.'

'Yes … well I suppose … we do have a cook.' Gladys couldn't help sounding doubtful. She'd always imagined she'd given up her job as a London parlourmaid to work as a missionary, not an innkeeper. But once Jeannie Lawson got an idea into her head there was no stopping her. Before the month was out, the Inn of Eight Happinesses was open for business. The roof had been fixed. The brick beds were warm. The smell of good food wafted, like bait, from the kitchen.

Unfortunately it was soon clear that the muleteers weren't biting. Clean beds or no clean beds, good food or no good food, they weren't going to risk body and soul staying in an inn run by foreign devils.

Something would have to be done to attract business.

'If the muleteers won't come here of their own accord, we – or rather you, Gladys – will just have to go out into the street and persuade them,' announced Jeannie.

'Other innkeepers do it,' she went on, turning to the window. 'Just watch.' A mule train was coming down the street. Gladys could see the head muleteer looking first one way and then another. 'He's trying to decide where to stay,' Jeannie hissed. Even as she spoke the decision was made for him. The proprietor of a nearby inn strode from his doorway, grabbed hold of the lead mule's head and within seconds the whole caravan was clip-clopping into his courtyard.

'You mean, you want *me* to do *that!*' Gladys gasped. 'But I *couldn't!*'

'Why not?'

'The mule might bite me.'

'The mule *won't* bite you.' Jeannie had never been very good at hiding her impatience.

To be on the safe side Gladys kept her hands firmly tucked into the wide sleeves of her blue jacket as she stood outside their front door next afternoon. Clip-clop … clip-clop. A mule train came swaying down the narrow street. She drew a deep breath, then in a rather shaky voice started to call out the words their Chinese cook had taught her – words supposed to draw customers like moths to a lamp.

'We have no fleas. We have no bugs. Good – good – good; come – come – come,' she called.

But despite the promise of so much goodness, nobody came. The muleteers ignored her and the caravan clip-clopped past.

A second train came into view. 'We have no fleas. We have no bugs. Good – good – good. Come – come – come,' Gladys called, more loudly this time.

Still no response.

Oh dear! It looked as if Jeannie was right. There was nothing else for it. As a third train appeared at the end of the street, the young woman took her hands out of her sleeves and tensed up like a spring. Clip-clop … clip-clop … the hoof-beats drew near. She could see the driver looking from side to side. The lead mule's head was level with their gateway.

'No fleas … no bugs … come – COME!' She leapt forward, grabbing the beast's ears, pulling its head in the direction of their courtyard. Next thing she knew, she was astride the animal's nose being carried between the gates.

The mule was inside. And where the lead mule went, the other mules followed. And where the mule train went, the muleteers and carriers followed – which meant, in short, that she had captured a whole caravan: seven mules, two drivers and around twenty carriers.

Nice work, Gladys! And now it was Jeannie's turn. No sooner had the inn's first customers been settled on the warm brick bed and served with basins of steaming dough strings than she bustled into the room, blue eyes sparkling.

'Don't be afraid.' She perched herself on the stool she'd brought with her. 'I've come to tell you a story. All the stories we tell at the Inn of Eight Happinesses are entirely free.'

The men looked interested in spite of themselves. Clean beds, good food, free stories. There was something to be said for the foreign devils' establishment after all.

'The story I want to tell you this evening is about a man called Jesus,' Jeannie began happily, and within minutes the storytelling session was in full swing.

Gladys sat nearby, quietly observing the look of rapt attention on the faces of their Chinese customers, thinking of another story – one Jesus had told – about a wedding feast. She now knew exactly how the servants in that parable had felt. It was easy to stick up signs and issue invitations. But there were times when you had to go out into the highway and haul your guests in.

EXTRA INFORMATION:

Gladys Aylward, the former parlourmaid, worked as a missionary in China for many years. During the war with Japan she led 100 homeless children on a twelve-day march over the mountains to safety. In 1957 a book, *The Small Woman,* was published about her achievement. It was translated into many languages and made into a film, *The Inn of the Sixth Happiness,* starring Ingrid Bergman

SUGGESTED SONGS:

Colours of day dawn into the mind (JP 28) (CPW 24) (K 433)

Come on, let's get up and go (JP 31)

Go, tell it on the mountain (JP 65) (CPW 54)

Tell me the stories of Jesus (JP 228)

The fields are white unto harvest time (JP 237)

We've a story to tell to the nations (JP 272)

We've got good news, good news, good news, good news (JP 362)

Let's go and tell our friends that Jesus cares (JP 416)

PART THREE

AROUND THE WORLD

Planting Norman

LENGTH: 4 minutes

TEACHING POINT: In the parable of the sower, God's word is compared to seed scattered on the ground. Are we allowing that seed to be planted in our lives?

BIBLE READING: Luke 8:4–8, 11–15

The people living on the islands of Guinea Bissau had a big problem. For the last few years their rice hadn't grown well. It hadn't grown well because there hadn't been enough rain. Harvest-time would come and instead of having fields full of golden stalks to cut down, they would find themselves looking at a scattering of spindly plants.

Norman, a missionary who'd come to live on the islands, thought he might have the answer to their problem. He'd studied agriculture at college, and after a lot of careful experiments, he'd found a strain of rice which would grow well even if it didn't get much rain. But there was another problem. The islanders believed that any change in the traditional way of doing things would upset the spirits. Change was dangerous – or so the witch-doctors said. They weren't going to approve of anyone doing anything different. Norman might have found a strain of rice which didn't need so much water to grow, but how was he going to persuade the farmers to plant it?

He'd been in Guinea Bissau long enough to know that rushing around handing out cartons of the seed would be a waste of time. So, to begin with, all he did was drop a hint or two in the ear of one local farmer – a man called Domingos Tubento.

'I may have some rice seed that will grow with less rain,' he mentioned to Domingos one day. 'The early results look promising.'

Domingos said nothing. He was a quiet man at the best of times. But he'd already gone against the witch-doctors. Years earlier he'd burnt his idols and broken with tradition to become one of the first Christian believers in Guinea Bissau. Norman knew that underneath this mild expression there was a very strong character.

The missionary left it a few months before paying the farmer another visit. This time he brought with him a little packet of seed. 'Here's that new kind of rice I was telling you about,' he said. 'Why not plant it in the corner of a field and see how it does?'

There was a long silence while Domingos thought this over. He took the container of seed and gave it a shake. He pursed his lips and chewed on his moustache. Then, slowly, he nodded. 'All right,' he said.

That year, once again, the rainy season stopped short. Once again all over the islands the rice was thin on the ground. But there was one exception. In one corner of one field people couldn't help noticing a splendid array of golden stalks. Can you guess who the field belonged to? Domingos Tubento. And of course village life being what it is, everyone knew the inside story. They'd all seen the white man visiting Domingos's hut. They'd all heard about the container of seed. They'd all been watching to see how it grew.

The following June Domingos sowed one whole field with the new seed.

In the villagers' eyes this was taking a huge risk. The spirits wouldn't like it. 'Oooo!' They clicked their tongues and predicted all sorts of disasters. Domingos's crops would be blighted. The spirits would strike him with some dreadful disease. But nothing like that happened. Instead Domingos had a bumper harvest.

By this stage three whole years had gone by since Norman had developed his new strain of rice. That November, when the missionary came to the village, he found Domingos out in the fields, deep in discussion with a group of local farmers. And to his surprise, his own name seemed to be on everyone's lips. 'Norman this … Norman that…' Unfortunately Norman didn't know the tribal tongue well enough to understand what they were saying. Was he in trouble? Had he offended someone?

'What was all that about?' he asked Domingos.

The farmer eyed him. 'They want to plant Norman.'

What! For a horrible moment the missionary pictured himself neck-deep in the swamp.

He needn't have worried. What those farmers had actually been discussing was the new strain of rice. Impressed by its performance, they'd needed to call it something to distinguish it from the old rice. So they'd christened it 'Norman'. What's more, they'd come to a decision. Praise God! They'd all be planting Norman that year.

SUGGESTED SONGS:

God is working His purpose out (JP 57)

God, whose farm is all creation (JP 61)

Our harvest day is over for yet another year (JP 193)

The fields are white unto harvest time (JP 237)

We plough the fields and scatter (JP 267)

At harvest time we celebrate (JP 311)

I'm going to hide God's Word inside my heart (JP 378)

It takes an almighty hand, to make your harvest grow (JP 395)

The Word of the Lord is planted in my heart (JP 473)

Mama Njina's Gift

LENGTH: 5 minutes

TEACHING POINT: Until Jesus broke the power of sin, the whole human race was condemned to die. Now, because of what he has done, those who trust him will live with him for ever.

BIBLE READING: Romans 5:6-8; 6:20-23

Monica was gathering wood in the forest. Cheerfully the ten-year-old girl knelt beneath the shady branches, adding sticks and twigs to her bundle. Birds called and chattered overhead. Then, suddenly, the happy rhythm of her daily routine was shattered. There was a cracking sound. 'Help!' Monica screamed as the ground gave way beneath her feet. It all happened so quickly she could do nothing to save herself. Next thing she knew she had plumeted to the bottom of a pit over two metres deep.

Shocked and breathless, the girl lay there in the darkness, fighting back tears. Her right leg felt as if someone was jabbing it with a knife and there was a warm stickiness trickling down to her ankle. She gazed up helplessly at the hole of light so high above her head. It would have been hard to climb out at the best of times. How would she ever manage it with an injured leg?

Fortunately a neighbour heard her desperate shouts. Mama Njina didn't waste any time. As soon as she saw Monica's plight, she jumped down beside her. But they weren't alone in the pit. There was a swift movement among the leaves, followed by a hiss. 'Ouch! A creature is biting me!' The woman felt a sharp pain in her calf. 'Oww! It bites me too!' Monica wailed, more anxious than ever to get out.

Mama Njina was a strong woman. (Kenyan women tend to be strong because they do so much hard physical work.) And now she lifted Monica by the waist and hoisted her towards the surface. 'Pull yourself up!' she urged. The girl caught hold of a clump of grass. Somehow between her own frantic scrabbling and Mama Njina's energetic pushing, she managed to heave herself onto the path.

By this stage a small crowd had reached the scene. 'Oh dear! This is very serious.' The villagers shook their heads at the sight of the deep gaping cut on Monica's leg. There was only one thing for it – the girl must be taken to Kijabe hospital.

Mama Njina, meanwhile, had scrambled out of the pit and dusted herself down. She didn't feel too bad. Her calf was still painful, but not sore enough to stop her preparing the evening meal. Having seen her little neighbour wrapped up in a blanket and on her way to Kijabe, she hurried off to get a pot of maize and beans on the fire.

Some hours later Monica reached the hospital, and the doctors and nurses swung into action. They were Christian people and the girl quickly realised that she was in safe hands. First she was taken to theatre to have her wound cleaned. Then she was brought to her bed on the children's ward. 'This is Alice, and this is Mwende,' a nurse said as she introduced her to some of the other children. Before long Monica was chatting happily to her new friends – telling them all about her adventure.

'Isn't your mother staying with you?' Mwende asked.

Monica shook her head. 'She must look after my brothers and my sisters.'

'Ah, that means you will be having many visitors,' Mwende smiled.

Sure enough, the very next afternoon Monica's relatives came to see her. But even though they were pleased to find her looking so well, they were the bearers of some very sad news.

There was no easy way of breaking it. Mama Njina was dead. The creature that had bitten her had been one of Kenya's most poisonous snakes – a black mamba.

'Mama Njina lay down after eating the evening meal last night.' Monica's grandfather made a pillow with his hands. 'She went to sleep and she is not waking up.'

Monica was too shocked for words. Mama Njina – bitten by a black mamba! Mama Njina – dead! Those terror-filled moments in the pit flashed through the girl's mind. That was when it had happened. And Mama Njina wasn't the only one to have been bitten. Did this mean she was going to die too?

It was a very unhappy, very frightened little girl left sitting up in bed that evening after the visitors had gone.

Seeing her troubled face, Vivien, one of the nurses, came to talk things over.

'You mustn't feel too sad about Mama Njina,' she said gently. 'It was a wonderful thing that she did.'

'She died from helping me,' Monica blinked back her tears. 'But … but now perhaps I will die too…' She pointed to the puncture marks on her leg.

Vivien shook her head. 'No, Monica, that bite is harmless. Mama Njina did more than help you. She saved your life. All the poison from the snake's fangs went into her body. There was nothing left to hurt you.'

Then, as the terrible fear faded from the child's eyes, she continued.

'It reminds me of what Jesus did when he took the poison of our sins into his body on the cross. He made death harmless.'

Thoughtfully Monica studied the bite on her leg. It didn't hurt at all now, and thanks to Mama Njina there would be no ill-effects. And here was this nurse telling her that thanks to Jesus it could be the same thing with death. Well, that was very fine.

She looked up with a beaming smile.

'Jesus offers us the gift of eternal life,' Vivien said softly. 'All we have to do is receive it.'

SUGGESTED SONGS:

Have you heard the raindrops drumming on the rooftops? (JP 71) (K 99)

I gotta home in gloryland that outshines the sun (JP 97)

I will sing the wondrous story (JP 127)

Jesus loves me! this I know (JP 140)

Low in the grave He lay (JP 159)

O Lord my God! when I in awesome wonder (JP 179)

Soon and very soon we are going to see the King (JP 221)

There is a green hill far away (JP 245) (K 725)

What a wonderful Saviour is Jesus (JP 274)

Yours be the glory! risen, conquering Son (JP 299)

Fire!

LENGTH: 5 minutes

TEACHING POINT: Non-believers are impressed when Christians stand firm under pressure. What sort of impression does our faith make?

BIBLE READING: Acts 16:16–34

Since their marriage, Bart and Eugenie had lived with their relatives in the family courtyard. Now, at long last, they'd moved into a house of their own. With its plain walls of home-made brick and corrugated iron roof it might not have looked much. But to Bart it was a dream come true.

The head of his clan hadn't wanted them to leave the courtyard. 'The spirits are evil on that side of the road,' he'd warned. 'Over there you'll get nothing but bad luck.'

He might as well have saved his breath. As Christian believers, Bart and Eugenie weren't worried about bad-tempered spirits. Alongside their modest brick house Bart had built a second building – a simple church with wooden walls, a wooden roof and benches. 'Come to the house of prayer,' he invited his friends and neighbours on Sunday mornings.

And then, as sometimes happens, just when everything seemed to be going so well, trouble came snarling out of the bushes. Bart discovered he needed an operation. No one welcomes that kind of news, but for a farmer who earns his money doing hard physical work the prospect of being out of action for several months was a terrible blow. As if that wasn't bad enough, the couple's baby daughter Benedicte took sick.

Perhaps you can guess what the superstitious villagers said when they heard about Bart's problems. 'The spirits are angry. That's why Bart is having bad luck.'

Living in a village is a bit like living in a goldfish bowl. Everyone watches everyone else. And now all eyes were on Bart and Eugenie to see what they would do. Would they try to win over the spirits they had angered? Would they consult a witch-doctor? Or even tie a little piece of black thread around the sick child's wrist to ward off curses? Not a bit of it. Sunday services in the house of prayer went on as usual. Bart made it clear that the only spiritual power he would turn to was the Christian God.

Next question: What would Bart's God do? The watching villagers saw nothing special to begin with. Slowly Benedicte got better. Little by little Bart's strength began to return. 'Just wait. There's more trouble ahead,' the relatives muttered darkly.

It came right out of the blue one otherwise peaceful March afternoon. Eugenie, not long returned from the cocoa plantation, was kindling a fire to cook the family meal when she saw her stepson, Aubin, running up the road to their home. Less than an hour ago she'd left him and his brother Huberson working with the cocoa pods. Now Aubin was breathless and glistening with sweat.

'Fire! Fire!' he cried.

This was one word every farmer dreaded to hear. A bushfire devoured all before it. Cocoa trees which had taken years to grow could be destroyed in minutes.

Aubin had brought news that the elephant grass was alight less than half a mile from their plantation, and Huberson was fighting alone to keep it from reaching the cocoa trees. Bart groaned with frustration as his wife and son raced from the house. It was only a few weeks since his operation. He was still too weak to walk down the path, never mind fight the blaze.

On reaching the plantation, a fearful sight met Eugenie's eyes. The fire was like a hungry monster: belching black smoke, shooting red flames high into the sky, gobbling up chunks of dried-up bush as it galloped greedily towards their crop.

A couple of men who farmed nearby had given up all hope of stopping it. They were leaning against their trees, sullen and helpless. But Eugenie was a fighter. 'Cut a swathe,' she yelled, hitching up her skirt and starting to hack frantically at the elephant grass that edged the plantation. Cutting a swathe meant clearing a strip of ground all around the property in the hope that the fire wouldn't leap over the bare earth.

It was a very faint hope, though – and Eugenie knew it.

Minutes passed. The roaring grew louder, the flames hotter, the smoke more dense. Still Eugenie hacked away, refusing to give in.

'See what your Jesus does for you!' one of the farmers shouted above the racket.

'If your Jesus saves your cocoa plantation we'll become Christians!' another farmer yelled.

Afterwards Eugenie couldn't have said whether it was minutes or just a few seconds later that God stepped in. But suddenly everything changed. It wasn't just that her own boys and some workers from a nearby school were hacking the grass beside her. Or that the wind had dropped. There was something more – something miraculous. The fire, which seconds earlier had been sweeping relentlessly in their direction, seemed to lose strength and speed. For the next twenty minutes it inched its way forward until, a few metres short of Bart's plantation, it fizzled to a halt and died.

You'd have thought, after saying they'd become Christians if God worked a miracle, the farmers who'd mocked Eugenie would have showed up in church that week. In fact they were nowhere to be seen. They probably heard the singing, though – the joyful voices of the twenty villagers who *had* come to Christ. They may even have heard Bart preach. Whether or not they were within earshot, one thing was certain. Bart and Eugenie's faith had impressed the whole village. And that Sunday the couple were praising God with all their hearts.

SUGGESTED SONGS:

Be still and know that I am God (JP 22)

Daniel was a man of prayer (JP 36)

God is our guide, our light and our deliverer (JP 56)

He who would valiant be (JP 80) (CPW 82)

How did Moses cross the Red Sea? (JP 83) (K 112)

In the name of Jesus (JP 111)

My faith is like a staff of oak (JP 168)

Christ be my leader by night as by day (JP 319)

It was Jesus who taught His disciples (JP 397)

The journey of life may be easy, may be hard (JP 468)

Raju's Birthday

LENGTH: 6 minutes

TEACHING POINT: Following Jesus means being willing to stop and help those in need.

BIBLE READING: Luke 10:29–37

In the years that Raju lived with his grandmother and his Uncle Ram, he never celebrated his birthday. He didn't even know when it was. Uncle Ram was a cruel man, and used to force the little boy to go out and beg for a living. Then, when Raju brought home a few coins, he would snatch them and complain because there weren't more. He didn't give Raju enough to eat. And sometimes he would lose his temper and hit him.

In the end the boy got so fed up with this treatment he decided to run away. But where could he go? He was only six years old and he had no other relatives to turn to. Then he remembered that down at the railway station there were a lot of children like himself living on the platform.

So, one evening, the little boy slipped out of the house and ran off to join them. From then on, instead of begging for his uncle, he spent his time collecting up old papers and plastic bottles to sell on to dealers. He earned enough most days to pay for one simple meal, and sometimes even a trip to the cinema. He often felt frightened, though – especially when policemen with their long canes came marching along the platform. Raju always ran away when he saw the police coming. But once he didn't move fast enough. 'People are sick of your pestering ways, you little beggar,' a tall officer said as he caught him. 'I'm taking you to the police station.'

The police station was horrible. The policeman made Raju say who he was and where he'd come from. Then he locked him up in a damp grey cell. 'We'll keep you here until your grandmother comes to collect you,' he said.

Raju's grandmother was none too pleased to find her long-lost grandson in a police cell. But she promised the policeman she would take him home and look after him. Raju hung his head, not knowing whether to be glad or sorry. Perhaps she really loved him after all. Perhaps things would be different. But they weren't. Back in the Bombay slums, Uncle Ram was as cruel as ever. So, once again, Raju ran off to the railway platform.

This time he discovered a new way of making money. He would sit with his back against the wall banging two shoe-brushes together until a pair of feet stopped in front of him. For two rupees he would polish the shoes on those feet until they gleamed. Cleaning shoes paid better than collecting plastic bottles and papers; but before long Raju's career as a shoe polisher came to an end. One morning, as he ran along the covered walkway, he slipped on a banana skin. Now that might sound funny, but it wasn't really, because when Raju slipped, he fell into a gutter and broke his wrist. Of course Raju didn't know his wrist was broken. He only knew it was very, very sore – far too sore even to lift a brush, never mind polish shoes. What was he to do? No work meant no money. No money meant no food.

That day, as usual, thousands of commuters made their way through the station to catch their trains. They all rushed past a small boy huddled at the side of the platform, crying with hunger and pain. Most of them didn't even see him. But towards the end of the rush-hour two ladies came along: typical Indian women – dark-eyed, dark-haired, dressed in the traditional long tunic and trousers. The wonderful thing was they didn't walk past. They stopped. They stopped because they'd seen Raju's tears and they wanted to help.

In the Bible Jesus tells a story about a man who behaved the same way. He was a Samaritan and he stopped to help a traveller who'd been beaten up by thieves.

'My name is Sapria,' the older of Raju's good Samaritans told him as she introduced herself. 'And this is Rena.' She pointed to her friend. 'We'd like you to tell us why you're crying.'

Raju gulped and held out his throbbing, swollen wrist.

'Oh dear! That's nasty.' Sapria and Rena looked really concerned. They chatted to one another briefly, then offered to take Raju to the doctor. The boy could hardly believe his ears. He'd never known such kindness. Medical treatment was expensive, but these two women were telling him not to worry. They would take care of the bill.

In Jesus' story the good Samaritan also took care of his injured traveller's bill. But Sapria and Rena went one better. Not only did they take Raju to the doctor and pay for the plaster to be put on his arm, a little while after their first meeting they brought the boy home to live with them.

'We know things are very hard for you, Raju,' they told him. 'But there is a God in heaven whose name is Jesus. He loves you and we believe he's telling us to open a home for children like you. So what do you say? Will you be part of our family?'

Brilliant! The boy jumped at the chance.

The next year was like a dream come true. For the first time in his life Raju had plenty of food to eat. He had clothes to wear. He was able to go to school.

And then came the day when he and his five new brothers sat in a circle on the floor and did something very special. In the middle of the circle were two plastic bags. One held little slips of paper on which Rena had written the numbers from one to thirty. The other held slips of paper on which she'd written the twelve months of the year. The two bags were passed around the circle and each boy took out one of the numbers and one of the months.

When Raju's turn came he shut his eyes and took a slip from the corner of each bag.

'What do they say? What do they say?'

'The number is seventeen and the month is July,' Sapria smiled.

'Hurrah!' Raju cheered.

Can you guess why he was so excited?

He'd just got his very own birthday. He still didn't know the actual date when he'd been born, but that didn't matter. The important thing was that the God who loved him had made him part of a family who loved him too. They've been celebrating his birthday on 17th July ever since.

SUGGESTED SONGS:

Would you walk by on the other side (JP 498)

When I needed a neighbour (JP 275) (CPW 232)

Kum ba yah, my Lord, Kum ba yah (JP 149)

There are hundreds of sparrows, thousands,
millions (JP 246) (CPW 206) (K 320)

Everyone in the whole wide world matters (JP 333)

There's a song for all the children (JP 478)

Jerusalem man, walking from his homeland (JP 405)

If you see someone lying in the road (JP 95)

Kidnapped!

LENGTH: 6–7 minutes

TEACHING POINT: The need to be persistent in prayer.

BIBLE READING: Luke 18:1–8

In a street on the outskirts of the city of Kathmandu twelve-year-old Ram kicked aimlessly at an empty tin can, wondering what to do next. Suddenly a truck rattled down the road towards him. With a screech of brakes and a belch of black smoke it pulled up at his side. Like all the trucks that travelled the steep roads between Nepal and neighbouring India it was a mass of colour. Tinsel glittered round its bumpers. Its sides were wildly painted in ornate designs. 'Hi there, sonny.' The driver poked his head out of his decorative cab, grinning toothily. 'Fancy a ride in my bus?'

What an offer! Ram didn't even own a bicycle. The thought of speeding down the street two metres above the ground brought a big smile to his face.

'You mean it?'

'Sure. Get in.' The driver leaned over, opened the passenger door and Ram hopped in beside him.

Of course it was a big mistake. There's a rule, isn't there? Don't take lifts from strangers. But remember Ram lived in Nepal, and he'd never been warned of the dangers of driving off with someone he didn't know. The engine revved up and away he went, bobbing up and down with excitement.

That was three o'clock in the afternoon. At six o'clock that evening Ram's mother, Bhawali, sent one of the younger children to fetch him for his evening meal. Life had been hard for Bhawali. Years earlier her husband had walked out, leaving her with a young family to bring up. Ram was her oldest child. He was a handful but she loved him dearly. So when the child came back saying his brother was nowhere to be found, Bhawali immediately went to look for him herself. 'Have you seen Ram anywhere?' she asked her friends and neighbours.

'No.' Everyone shook their heads. Then one neighbour remembered seeing the boy climb into a lorry. It had an Indian number plate, he recalled.

'A lorry from India!' Bhawali put two and two together and burst into tears. There were people in India willing to pay a lot of money for Nepali children. 'Ram's been taken to India. He's been kidnapped!' she wept.

Next morning Bhawali went to the school where she worked and told the headmaster what had happened. It was a small Christian school and everyone was very upset. Bhawali asked for time off to go and look for her son. 'Take as long as you need,' the headmaster urged her. 'We'll be praying for you and your boy.'

So Bhawali set off to search for Ram, and the school staff and pupils prayed that God would bring him home safely. But India is a huge country. For two whole weeks Bhawali searched. For two whole weeks the school children prayed – to no avail. In the end Bhawali gave up the hunt and returned to Kathmandu.

Everyone was very disappointed to see her back alone. Two pupils, Helen and Jane, were so sorry about Ram's disappearance that they decided to pray for him every day. Time passed. Other people stopped praying, but they kept it up. One month ... six months ... nine months. Soon the boy had been gone for over a year. Most people had forgotten about him by this stage, but not Helen and Jane. At some point every single day those two girls bowed their heads and prayed for his safe return.

Five hundred kilometres away, in the Indian town of Nagpur, one very miserable Nepali boy was working as a slave in an Indian household. How Ram wished he'd never got into that lorry! For the first few hours it had been a brilliant adventure, hurtling at break-neck speed down from the heights of Nepal into an exciting new land. But now his life was a relentless grind of domestic chores. He had to be up first thing every morning to get the fire going. He had to sweep the house, fetch the water, clean the vegetables, carry the shopping. It was the same old routine – day after day after day.

One morning, fifteen months after he'd been taken away from home, Ram was sent to the bazaar to buy some vegetables. As usual he had to jostle his way through the crowds. As usual he felt too tired and homesick to enjoy the colourful sights on every side. And then someone caught his attention: a figure wearing a yellow-and-orange Nepali cap, carrying two bags packed full of merchandise. He seemed familiar somehow. The boy's eyes narrowed. It looked like … no, surely it couldn't be. …

'Excuse me!' He pushed and shoved his way to the businessman's side. 'Excuse me but are you, by any chance, Ramesh the shopkeeper from Kathmandu?'

'I might be. Who's asking?' The man looked curious.

'Me. Ram. I'm from Kathmandu too,' Ram cried eagerly.

'So what's a Nepali boy doing in Nagpur?'

'I'm a slave. I got kidnapped.' The boy's lips quivered and his voice filled with longing. 'I really hate it here.'

'Well…' The shopkeeper frowned thoughtfully. Then he took Ram by the elbow. 'This way,' he said briskly. He'd come to Nagpur to buy stock for his shop, but by the look of things he would be bringing more than he'd bargained for back to Nepal.

So the lost son came home. Fifteen months after his disappearance Ram got off a bus, walked down the street and strode in through his own front door.

'Ram! Ram! You're back! I don't believe it.' Bhawali flung her arms around him, tears of joy streaking her cheeks.

And you can imagine how Helen and Jane felt when they heard the wonderful news. On one level it just seemed like an amazing coincidence – Ram's chance meeting with a kindly neighbour who was willing to pay his fare to

Kathmandu. But as someone once said, 'When I pray, coincidences happen. And when I stop praying, they don't.' Helen and Jane had never stopped praying. They'd kept asking God to watch over Ram. They'd been patient. They'd been persistent. They'd been faithful.

And God had answered their prayers.

SUGGESTED SONGS:

Ask! Ask! Ask! and it shall be given you (JP 11)

Daniel was a man of prayer (JP 36)

What a friend we have in Jesus (JP 273) (CPW 228)

Did you ever talk to God above? (JP 329)

His ways are not our ways (JP 364)

Prayer is like a telephone (JP 448) (CPW 176) (K 286)

Consequences

LENGTH: 5 minutes

TEACHING POINT: Breaking God's laws means living with the consequences.

BIBLE READING: Genesis 2:15–17; 3:1–24; Galatians 6:7–10

Daniel lived in Haiti, in a small house in the country. Monsieur Dupont lived in a bigger house next door. Monsieur Dupont's house was made of breeze-blocks with a corrugated iron roof. Daniel's house was made of mud and sticks with a thatched roof. Monsieur Dupont wore clean trousers, leather sandals, a new straw hat and a light jacket. Daniel wore dirty jeans, cheap plastic sandals, an old straw hat and a grubby, second-hand T-shirt with 'Shop till you drop' written on the back. Monsieur Dupont had a horse. Daniel hadn't. All in all

Monsieur Dupont was a lot better off than Daniel, and Daniel was jealous.

At that time there was a lot of trouble in the country. Different groups of armed men kept forcing their way into the presidential palace and taking over the government. Each time this happened there would be a period when law and order broke down. Roads were blocked. There were bursts of gun-fire in the streets. Some folk would seize the chance to settle old scores. In other words, if you felt someone had cheated or insulted you, you might turn round and *dechouquer* (pronounced *day-shoo-kay*) them. This meant you set fire to their property and put them out of their homes.

Now Monsieur Dupont was not a popular figure in his village. A number of people had grudges against him. And so, when the New Year brought yet another attack on the government, Daniel had a bit of a powwow with some friends. 'You know why Dupont's so well off, don't you?' Daniel told them. 'He used to be a member of the secret police.'

Hiss! Boo! Everyone hated the secret police. Of course Daniel had no proof that Monsieur Dupont *had* ever worked for them. But since nobody liked Dupont, his friends were all prepared to believe it.

'What are we waiting for? Let's go and *dechouquer* Dupont.' Armed with rocks, machetes and flaming torches, Daniel and his gang set off.

The operation went like clockwork. Monsieur Dupont knew the rules. When you saw a group coming to *dechouquer* you, you got out – fast! If he hadn't grabbed his gun – an old-fashioned rifle – there wouldn't even have been a scuffle. But he did – and there was. Bang! The gun went off. Monsieur Dupont made his escape. As he went, though, Daniel noticed a dark heap lying in the yard. There'd been a casualty. The bullet from the gun had killed Dupont's horse.

The next day dawned warm and sunny and Daniel went out to work in the fields. Every time he caught sight of Monsieur Dupont's empty house, he smiled to himself. No more Dupont. Brilliant! It wasn't until he returned home that evening that he realised things weren't quite as brilliant as they seemed.

Pooh! There was a faint smell in his yard – like blocked drains. Except Daniel's thatched hut didn't have any drains. For a moment the farmer couldn't imagine what the smell was – and then he remembered the dead horse. It was beginning to decompose.

Next morning the smell was worse, and soon the perfume of 'rotting horse' hung over the place like a poisonous cloud. By the end of the week it had taken over Daniel's life. It was the first thing he smelt when he got up in the morning and the last thing he smelt going to bed at night. He smelt it on his skin. He smelt it in his clothes. He tasted it in his food. 'This is unbearable,' he thought.

So he sent for his friends. 'Eugh, what a stink!' They stood round holding their noses and swatting flies. 'I need help to get that animal out of here,' Daniel explained.

His friends took one look at the horrible slimy body and shook their heads. They weren't touching it. No way.

'Why don't you go to the police?' one of them suggested.

This struck Daniel as rather a good idea. The police had a pick-up truck. All they had to do was load up the horse and drive off.

The local police base was a small butter-coloured hut at the side of the main road. Two officers sat outside, their black-booted feet up on stools, playing dominoes. 'There's a dead horse round my way needs moving,' Daniel told them. But to his disgust they didn't seem one bit interested. In fact they barely glanced up from their game.

'Look here,' said Daniel. 'That horse is a health hazard. It's your duty to move it.'

Now the policemen weren't stupid. They had a fair idea what Daniel had been up to. And at this one of them *did* look up. He looked Daniel straight in the eyes – a long hard look. 'So you want us to do our duty, do you?'

Ooops. Daniel might want the police to do their duty when it meant removing a dead horse. He did not want them to do their duty if it meant putting him under arrest. 'No … I mean yes … I mean. … never mind.' He took himself off.

What a mess! What a stupid horrible mess! Now the only way he could see of moving the horse was to pay someone to do it. And that would cost a packet.

The attack on the government was long over by this stage. The country had got back to normal. Daniel should have been out in his fields, looking after his crops. Instead he found himself fund-raising – standing out at a makeshift road-block, demanding money from drivers to let them pass through. It was a risky business. It was also very boring (sometimes there would be no cars for hours on end!). Knowing what he now knew, Daniel longed to turn the clock back – to un-*dechouquer* Dupont. But life doesn't work that way. You can't just turn round and wipe out wrong actions. There's a law of consequences, just like there's a law of gravity. People reap what they sow.

NOTE: Though the characters and many of the details in this story are fictitious, it is based on a true incident.

SUGGESTED SONGS:

Ask! Ask! Ask! and it shall be given you (JP 11)

Barabbas was a bad man (JP 18)

Don't build your house on the sandy land (JP 39) (CPW 38) (K 40)

O sinner man, where will you run to? (JP 194)

The wise man built his house upon the rock (JP 252) (CPW 205) (K 336)

Be careful little hands what you do (JP 312)

God in His love for us lent us this planet (JP 347)

It's not very nice saying 'Na na na na na na' (JP 401)

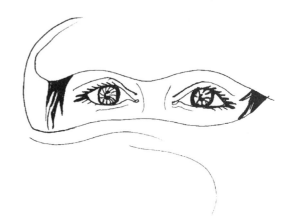

Faith Academy

LENGTH: 6 minutes

TEACHING POINT: Disappointments and set-backs test our faith, but the Bible shows what happens when people keep trusting God.

BIBLE READING: John 11:1–7; 28–41

The first thing five-year-old Miriam did each morning was wrap a cloth around her head and across the lower part of her face. This wasn't for protection from the sun, even though there was plenty of sunshine on the Philippine island where she lived. It was to stop people seeing her mouth. Miriam had been born with a split in her upper lip, known as a 'harelip'. It's a common enough problem, but the villagers didn't understand that. To them it looked evil, and they turned away in disgust.

And then one day Miriam's parents, Bernie and Jessie, came to her with some wonderful news.

'You remember the schoolchildren from Faith Academy who came to our island?' Jessie took the little girl on her knee.

Miriam nodded, picturing them: Ike, Allie, Chrissie, Stephen, Kate, and the rest. They'd come with their leaders, Hetty and Alan. They'd studied the volcano and swum in the volcanic lake. But the main thing Miriam remembered was how friendly they'd been – and how they'd let her join in their evening prayers and singsong round the fire.

'Since going back to school in Manila they've been thinking about you,' Jessie went on. 'They've raised money and fixed it so an organisation called Operation Smile sends a doctor to put a smile on your face.'

Miriam's sad eyes lit up. This was her dream – to be able to smile properly. But could it really happen? Cautiously, she raised a finger to her lips, tracing the ugly V-shaped split under her nose.

'Don't worry. You'll soon be rid of that,' Jessie assured her. 'We leave for Manila tomorrow.'

School dorm parents, Alan and Hetty, met the family off the bus.

'Miriam will spend the next few days preparing for surgery,' Alan explained on the way to the school. 'She'll have blood tests ... X-rays ... that sort of thing. All being well the first stage of Operation Smile will be completed within a fortnight.'

Two weeks! The little girl hugged herself in delight. Though 'harelip and facial reconstruction' was the official name for the surgery, Operation Smile definitely sounded better.

But a mere two days later the blow fell. Operation Smile was off. 'Your daughter can't possibly undergo surgery. Her general health is too poor.' The hospital doctor broke the bad news.

While Jessie and Bernie clung to one another in disappointment, Alan talked to the kids in his dorm.

'The problem is little Miriam has a bad case of TB,' he explained.

'But ... but. . . it doesn't make sense.' Everyone was devastated. They'd felt so sure that God had been telling them to help Miriam. So why had he allowed this to happen? Why raise the family's hopes only to shatter them?

There are no easy answers to those kinds of questions. Even when things didn't make sense, though, the pupils at Faith Academy had been taught to trust God. So, despite being confused and upset by the apparent failure of their plan, they didn't give up. They decided they would keep raising money. They would make sure Miriam got proper food and treatment until she was well enough for Operation Smile to go ahead.

Nobody knew how long that would take.

'Lord, please bless Miriam. Make her better. Be with her family,' the kids in Alan and Hetty's dorm prayed week after week. At the same time they held all sorts of fund-raising events to pay for the things Miriam needed: Ike washed cars; Chrissie helped organise a concert in the dorm; Stephen gave money regularly out of his allowance.

Every few months Miriam, her mum and dad, would come to Manila for her check-up. They would stay in the dorm with Hetty, Alan and the boarders, eating their meals and joining in dorm life. Each time they came the children prayed hard that Miriam would get the all-clear. But for two whole years that particular prayer remained unanswered.

Other things were happening, though. First Jessie and Bernie gave their lives to the Lord. Then they started going to church and studying the Bible. Then they began to hold a Bible study in their own home. Miriam, meanwhile, opened up like a flower in the sunshine. Things were so much happier at home now her mum and dad had come to faith; and, like them, she was learning about Jesus – the God who knew and loved her and made her feel beautiful inside.

So the years went by – during which time the schoolkids saw God change the life not just of one small girl but of her entire family circle. By the time Miriam's TB had cleared up even her grandparents were going to church.

Only then did Operation Smile take place.

'It's as if before giving Miriam her smile God wanted to make sure she really had something to smile about,' one of the kids remarked as they waited with bated breath to see their small friend after her surgery.

There was a sudden commotion downstairs. 'She's here!' Alan called.

This time there was no question of disappointment.

'Well, just look at you!' Ike, Chrissie and co. could hardly believe their eyes. Could this be the same skinny, straggly-haired youngster who had visited them so often? Miriam's hair was shining. Her eyes were sparkling. And as for her smile – well, her brand-new God-given smile said it all.

SUGGESTED SONGS:

Ask! Ask! Ask! and it shall be given you (JP 11)

My Lord is higher than a mountain (JP 170)

Now be strong and very courageous (JP 172)

The steadfast love of the Lord never ceases (JP 250)

Whether you're one or whether you're two (JP 284) (K 384)

And we know that all things (JP 310)

Can you be sure that the rain will fall? (JP 316)

Sometimes problems can be BIG (JP 461)

When you're feeling good put your thumbs up (JP 496) (K 382)

Spending Power

LENGTH: 4 minutes

TEACHING POINT: Material possessions don't last, spiritual possessions do.

BIBLE READING: Luke 12:15–21

Julio lived with his mother and grandmother and four brothers and sisters in a wooden house built on stilts. His granny had a stool and his baby sister had a hammock, but there wasn't any other furniture in the home. Julio slept and ate on the floor and kept his clothes in a plastic bag. Money was scarce, pocket-money unheard of. But on his fifteenth birthday the boy discovered what it felt like to be rich.

'Happy birthday, Julio. Hold out your hand and I'll give you your present,' Elizabeth smiled. (Elizabeth was a missionary who worked in Julio's church.) Into his palm she counted out fifteen ten-cent pieces – one for every year of his life. Excitedly the dark-eyed Guaymi Indian boy gazed down at the pile of coins. Julio was no brainbox. As a baby he'd had a serious illness which made it hard for him to learn. But he knew what fifteen ten-cent pieces added up to. A small fortune.

What should he do with it? Luxuries for Julio would have been a packet of biscuits or a handful of mints. Or a new notebook and pencil. Or a present for granny. But even as the possibilities raced through his mind, the boy knew he wouldn't be spending his money in the village shop. He wouldn't be saving it either. There was one thing he longed for above everything else.

With a broad grin, he handed the coins straight back to his missionary friend.

'Please can I have a Bible?' he said.

It's a fact that new Bibles can sometimes end up gathering dust. There was no chance of that happening to Julio's Bible. You don't lay out the largest sum of money you're ever going to have in your life to buy something and then not use it to the full. By the time he was seventeen Julio had one big ambition. He wanted to become a preacher. He knew passing the church exams would be difficult. But he was determined. And hardworking. And his missionary friend believed he might succeed.

The village where Julio lived overlooked the bay of Cusapin with its blue water, golden sand and coral reef. One day, a few months after his seventeenth birthday, Julio and a pal rowed out beyond the reef to fish for turtles. Turtle meat was tasty and they were hoping to catch a juicy specimen. Before long they spotted a dark shape gliding through the clear water.

'Here comes supper!' This turtle certainly promised a feast. It was almost one metre long. Eagerly the boys plunged their pointed sticks into the water. The idea was to catch the creature by digging the point in under its shell.

'Got him!' Julio hissed triumphantly. Now for the really tricky bit. It was one thing to have a turtle flailing on the end of your stick. It was another to manoeuvre the hefty creature into the boat – especially when the turtle put up a fight. And this turtle fought hard. It flapped. It wriggled. It had the two boys leaning as far as they could right out over the side of the boat.

And then, suddenly, the boat capsized. Both boys were trapped underneath. But Julio was unconscious – knocked out by a blow to the head. Desperately his friend struggled to free him. In the end, though, he was forced to swim to the surface alone. He raised the alarm, but it was too late. Just like that – without any warning – one bright June afternoon Julio was dead.

In Luke's Gospel Jesus tells a story about a man who, like Julio, died suddenly and unexpectedly. Like Julio, he'd been full of plans. But there the similarity ends. For the man in the story had only planned for this present world. Death robbed him of everything. And Jesus said he was a fool.

No one could have said that about Julio. When he died, the whole village wept. But in their grief the boy's family and friends were comforted to think of the store of spiritual riches waiting for him in heaven. He'd left behind one well-thumbed Bible – the book that had helped prepare him for eternity. Fifteen ten-cent pieces had never been more wisely spent.

SUGGESTED SONGS:

A boy gave to Jesus five loaves and two fish (JP 1)

I do not know what lies ahead (JP 92)

Put your hand in the hand of the man who stilled the water (JP 206)

Said Judas to Mary, 'Now what will you do . . .' (JP 211)

Seek ye first the Kingdom of God (JP 215) (CPW 182) (K 292)

Tell me the old, old story (JP 227)

Turn your eyes upon Jesus (JP 260)

When I survey the wondrous cross (JP 277)

If your empty tum is rumbling (JP 390)

Smokey the Bear

LENGTH: 8 minutes

TEACHING POINT: God created us as human 'beings' not human 'doings'. In the middle of all our activities we need time to be together with one another, and to be together with him.

BIBLE READING: Luke 10:38–42

Eight-year-old Leanne's favourite toy was a battered teddy bear called Smokey. Smokey sported a navy-blue park ranger's uniform with a wide-brimmed hat and a big shiny badge. All over the States, brand-new Smokeys, dressed in exactly the same uniform, had been produced by the fire service to remind children about preventing forest fires. But even though there were so many Smokeys around, Leanne's Smokey was special. Those other bears might know a lot about fire prevention, but only Leanne's bear knew all about Leanne.

Leanne and Smokey did everything together. So naturally the year the Heath family went caravanning in Kentucky, Smokey went caravanning too.

Apart from Smokey there were five family members on holiday with Leanne that summer. There was her mum, her dad, her older sisters Julie and Lisa and her granny. And between them they had a lot of different ideas about what holidays were for.

Mr and Mrs Heath thought holidays were for rushing around seeing as many sights as possible. This meant that they aimed never to spend more than one night in any one place. Julie and Lisa thought holidays were for swimming and meeting boys. This meant they wouldn't allow Mr Heath to stop at a campsite unless it had a swimming-pool. Granny Heath believed that holidays were for falling asleep in the back of the car. This meant she spent her time snoring very loudly. As for Leanne – well, Leanne *had* thought holidays were for enjoying yourself. But she certainly wasn't enjoying this one.

Day after day she found herself squashed in the car with her snoring grandmother on one side and her squabbling sisters on the other. 'Does that site have a swimming-pool?' they would yell whenever Mr Heath found a likely place to stop. If there wasn't a swimming-pool they made him drive on – for hours it seemed – until he found one. It wouldn't have been so bad if Leanne had liked swimming-pools. But she didn't. She couldn't swim.

So the week went by, with Leanne becoming more and more fed up. Each day was horrible, but somehow out of all the horrible days, the day before they were due to go home was the worst. It was terribly hot. The sights were terribly boring. Granny snored terribly loudly. And as usual her sisters spotted a terribly good-looking boy at the swimming-pool and left her sitting, like a prune stone, on the edge.

'Know something, Smokey – I *hate* holidays,' Leanne whispered in Smokey's ear. All she wanted to do after tea was curl up in bed.

'Goodnight,' she called gloomily, trailing off towards the van.

'Goodnight, sugar,' her dad called after her. 'I'll be in in a minute to tell you a story.'

This was the first piece of good news Leanne had had all day. Her dad told brilliant bedtime stories. He made them up himself – all about Smokey and his adventures. 'Will it be a Smokey story?' she checked.

'Sure thing. Just give me a few minutes to sort out the route home.'

Now you may have noticed this about adults, but often when they ask you to give them a few minutes, they really mean a few hours! And that was the way it was with Mr Heath and his route home. Leanne waited and waited. But there was no sign of her dad. In the end she fell asleep without her bedtime story.

The journey home next morning got off to a bad start. The whole family overslept. 'Jumping jellybeans! It's gone nine o'clock!' Mr Heath rocketed out of his bunk and started chivvying everyone out of the caravan and into the car. 'There's no time for breakfast. We're way behind schedule. We'll grab something to eat on the road.'

One good thing about tumbling straight out of bed into the car is that your body doesn't get a chance to wake up. Leanne, Julie, Lisa and Granny (of course!) all dozed peacefully through the first part of the journey. It wasn't until they had been travelling for a couple of hours that Leanne suddenly realised something wasn't quite right. She felt around, but no furry body came to hand. She sat up. She hunted all over the back of the car. 'Mom, where did you pack Smokey?' she called. 'I can't find him anywhere.'

There was a sudden screech of brakes.

'We're having an accident. We're having an accident.' Julie and Lisa clutched each other blindly.

But they weren't having an accident. Mr Heath had simply pulled in suddenly to the side of the road.

'I feel terrible.' He banged his head against the steering-wheel.

'Are you ill, honey?' cried Mrs Heath, full of concern.

'No. It's what I've just *done*.' And out it all came. The previous night after Leanne had fallen asleep he'd remembered about the bedtime story. He'd been mad with himself for breaking his promise. So he'd taken Smokey and put him up a tree outside the caravan.

'I planned on Leanne discovering him this morning. And then I was going to tell her this really neat story to explain how he got there. Only in the rush to get on the road I forgot ... .'

'Are you saying that Leanne's teddy is stuck up a tree a hundred miles away?' said Julie.

Mr Heath nodded and Leanne burst into tears.

'Oh Smokey! My Smokey! I'll never see him again,' she sobbed.

'Right. That's it!' Mr Heath started the engine and turned the car.

'Hey, where are we going, Pop?' Julie and Lisa cried.

'Where does it look like? We're going back to the campsite to get Smokey – that's where.'

'I don't believe this!' Mrs Heath shook her head. 'We're travelling back one hundred miles to get a *bear!*'

The million-dollar question in everyone's mind was whether Smokey would still be up that tree when they got there. And it was a big relief to reach the place where they'd parked their van and see a threadbare paw poking out between the branches. 'Down you come, pal.' Mr Heath fished the bear out of his hiding-place and handed him to Leanne.

'Oh Smokey, did you miss me? I *really* missed you,' she said as she hugged him close.

Meanwhile her parents were trying to work out what to do next.

'We'll never make it home now,' Mrs Heath pointed out.

'That's true,' Mr Heath agreed, looking thoughtful. 'You know, somehow this Smokey business has made me think. Maybe we've been doing too much rushing around. Maybe we should extend our vacation, and just... well... *be* together, as a family.'

So that's what they did. For the first time since leaving home the Heath family spent three whole days in the one place – no rushing around, no driving, no sightseeing. There was time for playing games, having fun, telling stories. And after three days of *being* together everyone felt better.

'Know something, Smokey?' Leanne whispered in her teddy's ear when they finally bundled into the car to drive home. 'Thanks to you this has been a pretty neat holiday after all!'

SUGGESTED SONGS:

Abba Father, let me be (JP 2) (CPW 4) (K 3)

Behold, what manner of love the Father has given unto us (JP 15)

Be still and know that I am God (JP 22)

He brought me to His banqueting house (JP 73)

I'll be still and know that You are God (JP 93)

The greatest thing in all my life is knowing You (JP 239)

A naggy mum, a grumpy dad, a brother who's a pain (JP 302)

Jesus put this song into our hearts (JP 408) (CPW 129) (K 209)

Sometimes I'm naughty (JP 460)

First Things First

LENGTH: 4–5 minutes

TEACHING POINT: In the book of Haggai God rebukes his people for living in well-built houses while his Temple lies in ruins. When faced with a choice between looking after ourselves and doing something for God, which do we choose?

BIBLE READING: Haggai 1:1–15; John 6:1–14

Rodrigo lived on the outskirts of the Brazilian town of Porto Velho. Jardin das Mangueiras the area was called. The name means 'garden of mangoes' and conjures up pictures of luscious fruit and beautiful scenery. In reality the boy's home was one of thirty wooden shacks erected on an expanse of waste ground.

There weren't any mangoes, and if the wealthy landowner who farmed nearby had had his way there wouldn't have been any shacks either. 'Clear off!' he'd told the shack-dwellers. 'Jardin das Mangueiras is mine. I've papers to prove it.' Fortunately Rodrigo's church leaders had come to the rescue, going to the government and buying a plot of ground right in the middle of Jardin das Mangueiras.

'The fact that they could buy it proved the landowner's papers were forged,' Rodrigo's parents explained. 'He can't evict us now. We're safe.'

It was then, perhaps, that the first seeds of a special plan took root in the boy's mind. Now he knew his family weren't about to be evicted from Jardin das Mangueiras, he could dream of replacing their flimsy shack with something more permanent. All he needed was a little determination and a lot of bricks.

So, while the church leaders discussed how they would develop their plot of land, Rodrigo dreamt of living in a brick-built house.

Stopping at a building site on the way home from school one day he took careful note of the builders' technique. He saw how they filled the hollow tubes in the smooth shiny bricks with concrete before placing them end-to-end along the walls. (Brazilian bricks are bigger than the bricks we use and also more expensive.) They were building a bungalow – just the sort of bungalow he wanted for himself. Stirred to action, the boy picked out the friendliest-looking builder and made his approach.

'Hello,' he said brightly. 'My name's Rodrigo. Can I have a brick?'

'A brick?' The builder straightened up, wiping his brow, his eyes twinkling a question. What did this ten-year-old lad want with a brick?

'Please … .' Rodrigo flashed him a pleading smile.

'Oh all right then.' The man selected a single brick from the pile at his side. It was slightly chipped so he wasn't planning to use it.

'Thanks a million!' Rodrigo took the brick, thrust it into his school-bag and away he went.

'I got a brick today,' he announced proudly the minute he got home.

'Ace!' cheered Gleison, his eight-year-old brother. Obligingly he fished the brick out of Rodrigo's school-bag and carried it round to the back of the shack.

The following Sunday a special service was held in their church. Pastor Roberto was talking about the church plans for Jardin das Mangueiras.

Eagerly Rodrigo and Gleison listened as those plans were unveiled.

'We want to build a church in Jardin das Mangueiras – a multi-purpose building that will be a community centre too. That way, as well as Sunday services, we can run health programmes and children's clubs and an agricultural project,' the pastor explained.

A children's club. Ace!

'We have a team of builders ready to start,' Pastor Roberto went on. 'What we don't have is building materials.' He paused and looked at the congregation. 'So tonight I'm asking for pledges. Around 3,000 bricks are needed to build God's house in Jardin das Mangueiras. I would like you all to think about this, and promise the number of bricks God lays on your heart.'

There was a moment of silence during which Rodrigo flashed Gleison a look. The younger boy nodded. And Rodrigo's hand shot up.

'Please, Pastor Roberto, my brother and I promise 200 bricks.'

Two hundred bricks! Roberto blinked, wondering if he'd misheard. How on earth were two penniless schoolboys going to get their hands on 200 bricks? 'Why thank you, Rodrigo.' He hid his astonishment, mentally deciding to have a word with the boys' mother.

For the second time the brothers exchanged grins. They were well aware that a lot of eyebrows had been raised. A lot of people were wondering how they could possibly honour their pledge. What those folk didn't know was that every day for the past fourteen months Rodrigo and Gleison had been scavenging building-sites and builders' yards on their way home from school. Some weeks they'd got no bricks. Other weeks they'd gleaned three or four. And that very week Rodrigo's friendly builder had contributed brick number 200 to the pile. Yes, *all* the promised materials were already neatly stacked outside the boys' shack. Of course until now the lads had been planning to use them to build their own house. But that dream could wait.

The house for God's work must come first.

SUGGESTED SONGS:

A boy gave to Jesus five loaves and two fish (JP 1)

God, whose farm is all creation (JP 61)

I met Jesus at the crossroads (JP 102)

Just as I am, Your child to be (JP 146)

Seek ye first the Kingdom of God (JP 215) (CPW 182) (K 292)

The greatest thing in all my life is knowing You (JP 239)

The wise may bring their learning (JP 253)

Ah Tee's Secret

LENGTH: 4–5 minutes

TEACHING POINT: God wants us to share his love with those closest to us – but we need to make sure we're showing it first!

BIBLE READING: John 3:1–2; 19:38–39

It was 7.00 am on 1st January, and Tan Ah Tee was getting ready for his first day at secondary school. Eagerly he pulled on his long blue school trousers, feeling tall and grown-up. Until now, like all primary school pupils in Singapore, he'd dressed in red shorts.

Mr and Mrs Tan smiled proudly when they saw him.

'You'll get a good education in the church school, Ah Tee,' his mother said. 'But remember, your father and I don't want you singing Christian songs and reading Bible stories. The Christian religion is for foreigners.'

Ah Tee shifted uncomfortably – something his mum put down to the stiff new trousers.

'It's almost 7.15,' the boy said quickly. 'I'd better go.'

'Why did life have to be so difficult?' he thought as he made his way towards the grey school building. His mother was worried about him *attending* a church school. How could he ever tell her he'd become a Christian?

The church school was a brand-new building. Everyone – teachers included – spent the first week of term struggling to find their way around. The wonderful thing, though, as far as Ah Tee was concerned was that he kept bumping into other Christians. For the first time since getting to know Jesus at a children's club the previous year he didn't feel an odd man out. At last he had the chance to talk over the problems of being a secret believer with people who understood.

'Just concentrate on praying for your parents and sister to begin with,' one teacher advised. 'God knows all about you, and he loves you and your family very much.'

A few weeks later came the Chinese New Year – a big family celebration in Singapore. This was the time when everyone said sorry for the wrong things they had done and when houses and flats were swept out to get rid of the bad luck from the previous year. Of course Ah Tee didn't believe in bad luck now – but he could still spot a few holes in his behaviour.

'Sorry I teased you,' he said to his sister, Ah Chiu.

'Sorry I didn't tidy the bedroom,' he told his mum.

He began to pray that God's love would work in his home – and before long he could point to some encouraging results. Now that he was praying for his mum he was more likely to notice when she looked tired, and to spot things he could do to help her. Now that he was praying for his dad he no longer needed reminding ten times before he did what Mr Tan asked. Now that he was praying for his sister he didn't feel the same urge to wind her up. In other words, the new year had seen a dramatic change in his behaviour.

'What's he looking for?' Ah Chiu wondered.

'What's got into him?' Mr and Mrs Tan asked.

Time and again it was on the tip of Ah Tee's tongue to tell them about his faith. But somehow he could never quite find the words to explain.

'In school when we have discussions, I've more to say than anyone else. Yet at home I'm tongue-tied,' he told his Christian friends. 'Sometimes I feel as if I'm letting God down.'

'No you're not. Your actions are saying more than 1,000 words,' the school chaplain told him. 'And the right moment to tell your parents will come … .'

A few weeks later Ah Tee was sitting round the table with his family for the evening meal.

'Anything to report?' Mr Tan inquired.

He asked the same question most days. But today instead of his usual careful response Ah Tee found himself taking a deep breath. 'Well, yes – there is something,' he said calmly. 'There's a Christian service in school on Sunday. I became a Christian last year and I'd really like to go.'

If he was surprised at his own courage, he was even more surprised at his parents' reaction. He'd expected them to be furious. In fact they took the whole thing very well.

'Jesus isn't our religion,' his father pointed out. 'And we'd prefer you to follow us. Still, we are very happy with your progress in school.'

'And we appreciate what a good, respectful boy you are at home,' his mother added.

'So,' Mr Tan finished, 'we're willing to let you attend these Christian services for a while and see how it goes.'

That Sunday Ah Tee left the flat walking on air. Truly God's love had worked wonders. Here he was going to his first ever church service.

But best of all, his secret was out!

SUGGESTED SONGS:

Be bold, Be strong (JP 14) (CPW 11) (K 17)

Brothers and sisters in Jesus our Lord (JP 21)

Come on, let's get up and go (JP 31)

In our work and in our play (JP 108)

Keep me shining, Lord (JP 147)

This little light of mine (JP 258) (K 343)

It's the little things that show our love for Jesus (JP 403)

Heart Transplant

LENGTH: 5 minutes

TEACHING POINT: Sin makes our hearts hard. But Jesus wants to forgive our sin and fill them with his love.

BIBLE READING: Ezekiel 36:26

What would you do if you saw TV shots of enemy soldiers burning down villages and knew your village could be next?

Here's what thirteen-year-old Demë did. He hid his fear and pretended things would get back to normal soon.

What would you do if your Dad told you that you must leave your house, your school, your possessions and your friends because it wasn't safe to stay?

Here's what Demë did. He hid his sadness, squared his shoulders and packed what he could.

Demë lived in the land of Kosovo. When war broke out, like thousands of other families, his family fled for their lives. This was bad but what came next was even worse. 'Where's Papa? What's happened to him?' Demë's younger sisters and brother kept asking. 'I don't know.' Their mother gazed helplessly out of the window, trembling and fiddling with her shawl. Demë's father had gone out to buy bread that morning and had not returned. Somehow the boy fought back the terrible dread that clutched at heart. With Papa gone, he had to be strong. He needed to act like a man.

Demë became so good at toughing things out that after a while he hardly realised he was doing it. He kept his guard up even on the red letter day when his Dad came home. His mother and sisters cried for joy and threw their arms around each other. But for Demë, this wasn't a time for hugs and kisses. It was a time for hating the men who'd beaten Papa up and left him for dead.

His anger continued when the war ended and the family was able to return to their village. For Demë this wasn't a time for celebration. It was a time for hating the men who'd looted their comfortable home and turned it into a wreck.

Months went by and the family struggled to rebuild their lives, sleeping and living together in the single room that Papa had managed to repair. 'Run! Run! They're coming to get us,' Demë's sisters would call out in the night. They all had nightmares. The boy could hardly remember a time when fighting and gun fire didn't fill his dreams.....

Then, one afternoon Demë's brother said, 'Fancy a trip to the high school?'

'What do you want to go there for?' asked Demë.

'There's a group of Americans doing stuff with the kids. They've started a club with singing and games...'

'A kids'club!' Demë snorted. 'I don't think so!'

But the truth was he had nothing better to do – so he went.

Almost before he knew it, he was part of a large crowd of children and young people gathered in a grassy clearing.

'Hi! My name's Linn and. I'm taking names for the football tournament. Can I put you down as a forward?'

The speaker was a middle-aged lady with smiling blue eyes.

'Er…well…OK!' Demë hadn't planned to get involved, but somehow this lady drew him in. She seemed so glad to see him….so keen that he should have fun.

So it came about that that afternoon, for the first time in months, Demë forgot about the war. That afternoon he knocked a ball about, laughed and listened to the visitors talk about Jesus. One thing he couldn't help noticing was the gentle warmth in the way they acted and spoke.

Back he came the next day and the next day and the next. Soon he knew all the team members by name. Linn, though, was the one he knew best.

'Any chance that I could meet the rest of your family before I leave?' she asked towards the end of the week.

'Sure. Come home with me for coffee.'

'Your folks won't mind?'

'Course not.' The boy shook his head.

Just as he expected, his Mum received Linn gladly. She sat their visitor down on the least uncomfortable seat in the room and set a can of water on a primus stove to boil. And then something happened which the boy found quite amazing. Linn looked round the room and went very quiet. Next thing she was fumbling for a tissue. He saw tears roll down her cheeks. 'She's crying!' Demë marvelled. 'Crying because my family has to eat, sleep and cook in this one room. She's crying because she cares.'

Demë felt quite sure he could never care about strangers like that. Why, sometimes he felt as if he didn't even care about friends. 'My heart is hard,' he thought. 'But hers is soft.' The boy found himself remembering what Linn and her friends had taught him about Jesus – and it was as if he'd arrived at a door - a door which he could choose to open or not. 'I need to make up my mind about what I'm going to do with my life,' he thought. 'Should I stay like this? Cold, with no love in my heart. Or should I open up to Jesus?'

Opening his heart to Jesus would be costly. It would make him different from his family….different from his mates…different from almost everyone else in his village. Yet that summer fourteen-year-old Demë opted for a spiritual heart transplant. He gave his life to Christ and he has never looked back. God used a woman weeping in the shell of his house to show him how the shell of his heart could be changed.

SUGGESTED SONGS:

Ask! Ask! Ask! and it shall be given you (JP 11)

I have decided to follow Jesus (JP 98)

Make me a channel of Your peace (JP 161) (K 248)

Seek ye first the Kingdom of God (JP 215) (CPW 182) (K 292)

I'm going to take a step of faith (JP 381)

PART FOUR

INTO GOD'S WORD

Eavesdropping

LENGTH: Basic story 6 minutes. (You will need to allow extra time to organise and cue in sound effects.)

TEACHING POINT: The Israelites' grumbling was a sign of their lack of faith in God. Real faith goes hand in hand with thankfulness and praise.

BIBLE READING: Numbers 21:4–9; John 3:14–17

We've travelled back in time. It's the year 3200 BC. We're in the desert with Moses and the children of Israel – and we're about to do a little research.

But first, some background information. The men, women and children out here in the desert are God's chosen people and he's taking them to a land of their own. They've seen miracles. For example, food is hard to come by in these parts. But six days a week for the last thirty-eight years these folk have found a fresh supply of manna waiting outside their tents every morning. God's never failed to deliver. They collect it when they get up. Then pound it into flour, boil it and make it into flat cakes that taste like honey-flavoured bread.

So the question we're researching is this: Do these Israelites really appreciate God's goodness to them?

Let's find out, shall we? Shut your eyes and imagine you're tuning in to a conversation between a rather podgy Levite and his wife.

Man: I'm starving. What's for tea?

Woman: What do you think? Manna. You can have it raw or baked.

Man (groaning): If I have to look at one more plateful of the stuff I think I'll throw up. I dreamt last night of the food we ate in Egypt – cucumbers, watermelons, onions, fish and garlic, corn cakes and honey…

Woman: Stop! I can't bear it! We must have been mad, leaving all that for this.

Man: I blame Moses. He should have warned us what we were letting ourselves in for.

Woman: That's right. I hate manna. I blame Moses too.

Oh dear! By the sound of things there isn't much gratitude to God in that particular tent. But maybe it's a question of age. Maybe that couple are grumpy because they're a bit old for desert life. I know! Let's tune in to a group of young people and hear what they have to say.

Israelite young people: Moses is a meanie. Moses is a meanie.

Another disappointing result. But we'll give it one last try. We'll move on to the children. Surely the children will appreciate God's goodness.

Israelite children: Oh no! Not manna again! Oh no! Not manna again!

Well, that's that. The children are complaining too. It really looks as if we've travelled back 5,000 years only to find ourselves in the middle of a nation of grumblers.

Now if you're squeamish or given to nightmares this is the moment to zoom back to the twentieth century because you *could* find the next part of this story upsetting. It features snakes. Hundreds of them.

Come in, the snakes. *(Snakes hiss.)*

All of a sudden our grumpy Israelites have a lot more to grumble about than boring old manna for dinner. There's a plague of snakes in the camp. They're slithering around everywhere – under stones, round poles, into tents. There's just no avoiding them. What's more, they're sinking their fangs into people right, left and centre. And worst of all, their bites are deadly.

So what's going on?

Well, these snakes are God's way of letting his people know that he's heard their grumbles, and that, in his eyes, griping about the food and complaining about their leader is a serious sin. 'Let's be quite clear about this,' he's saying. 'What you're really doing is grumbling against me.'

There's nothing like a good dose of snake venom to make people aware of their faults.

No sooner do the vicious vipers strike than a delegation of apologetic Israelites come knocking on the door of Moses' tent.

'We sinned when we complained about God and blamed you.' They hang their heads. 'Please ask God to take these snakes away.'

Moses sighs. It's not the first time this sort of thing has happened and he knows his Israelites too well to imagine it will be the last. A less patient man would have given up on them years ago. But not Moses. Moses is one of the most dedicated leaders who has ever walked the face of the earth. So he doesn't remind the Israelites that they've done nothing but complain since the moment they left Egypt. He doesn't say that as far as he's concerned they all deserved to be bitten to death. He goes and prays for them. And, as always, when this dedicated leader prays, God answers.

'Make a metal snake and put it on a pole,' God tells him. 'When the people who are bitten look at it, they will be healed.'

So Moses makes his bronze snake, and puts it up on a pole where everyone can see it. Next thing the people who've been lying at death's door begin to get their strength back. Before you can say hallelujah they're skipping around the desert. 'Hey, look guys, God's healed us! All the poison has left our bodies!'

What *they* don't know is that a few thousand years down the line God has a much greater spiritual healing in store. We're at an advantage there. We can receive it! Living towards the end of the second millennium we know all about Jesus and about the new life that comes from him.

So we'll leave the Israelites rejoicing in their healing and return to our own century. As we go, though, let's ask ourselves a question. Let's imagine some of our Israelite friends decide to come with us. Let's imagine they want to find out how twentieth-century Christians behave – whether, like them, we spend our time grumbling or whether we're full of thankfulness for all that God has done. Let's imagine they join our family circles and eavesdrop on our conversations. The question is: What will they hear?

TELLING THIS STORY TO A GROUP:

Prepare for this story by making a recording of the conversation between the Israelite couple to be played at the appropriate moment in the narrative. (Alternatively, you could arrange to have it acted out.) Before beginning to tell the story divide a section of children into three groups – Israelite young people, Israelite children and snakes. Rehearse sound effects as follows: Israelite young people chant 'Moses is a meanie'; Israelite children repeat 'Oh no! Not manna again!'; Snakes hiss. Tell story introducing these sound effects as indicated.

SUGGESTED SONGS:

God is good, we sing and shout it (JP 55) (K 74)

Have you seen the pussy cat, sitting on the wall? (JP 72) (CPW 78) (K 100)

How did Moses cross the Red Sea? (JP 83) (K 112)

It's a happy day and I praise God for the weather (JP 118)

Oh! Oh! Oh! how good is the Lord (JP 180) (K 266)

Praise Him, praise Him, all you little children (JP 201)

Are you humbly grateful or grumbly hateful? (JP 309)

Even if I don't like the way things went today (JP 330)

Give thanks to the Lord for He is good (JP 345) (K 471)

It's not very nice saying 'Na na na na na na' (JP 401)

Winning God's Way

LENGTH: Basic story 7 minutes. You will need to allow extra time for rehearsing and cuing in group sound effects.

TEACHING POINT: God's victories are won through faith, obedience and love.

BIBLE READING: This story is based on Joshua 6:1–20. You may also wish to refer to Ephesians 6:10–18.

The Israelites have crossed the River Jordan and entered Canaan. There before them is the walled city of Jericho which they must capture to gain a firm foothold on the land.

'Here's the good news!' says their leader Joshua. 'God has promised to deliver Jericho, with its king and all its brave soldiers, into our hands.'

'Hurrah!' cheer the Israelites.

'But here's the bad news. It won't be straightforward.' Instead of giving his soldiers the command to go ahead and storm the place, Joshua gives them some extra training.

First he gets seven priests to practise their trumpet-blowing.*T

Then he gets everybody to practise their marching.*A

Finally – and this is the worst bit – they all have to practise keeping quiet. Joshua orders them to say nothing for ten whole seconds.*A

'Trumpets, marching and keeping quiet are the weapons God wants us to use to fight this battle,' he explains when the ten seconds are up. 'We're to march round the city *silently* once a day for six days. The only noise will be the sound of seven trumpets. On the seventh day we march round six times. And then, just as we're about to march round for the seventh time, we all shout at the top of our voices. Is that clear?'

The soldiers nod gloomily. It may be clear – but it doesn't make sense. You don't capture a city by parading around it like an army of mice. No way!

But according to Joshua these are God's instructions so there's nothing more to be said. First thing on Sunday morning the Israelites launch their non-attack. Left... right... left... right... They march down to Jericho. Out in front is the advance guard.*AG Then come the seven trumpeting priests.*T More priests, carrying the covenant box, come next, with a second battalion of soldiers bringing up the rear.*RG Ta... tat... tara... rara... Left... right... left... right... Wordlessly, they march round the city walls.

On Monday and Tuesday they go through the same routine all over again. The priests blow trumpets. The soldiers march. Nobody speaks.

By Wednesday the inhabitants of Jericho have started to poke fun at the ritual. As soon as they hear the sound of trumpets and marching feet they leap onto the ramparts and jeer at the passing Israelites. *'Cowardy, cowardy knock knees. Couldn't fight for fig trees,'* they chant – which is hard to take. When someone shouts at you, you feel like shouting back. But the Israelites can't shout back. God has told them not to.

On Thursday and Friday things go from bad to worse. Dozens of enemy soldiers crowd onto the city ramparts. Before long their taunts are so loud they drown the Israelite trumpets. *'Cowardy, cowardy bird brains. Couldn't fight for sugar canes.'*

Marching past without taking action is torture – like having a fly on the end of your nose and not being able to swipe it. Yet somehow Joshua's men resist the temptation to yell and fling their spears.

'Lord, I hope you know what you're doing,' Joshua prays that night. 'My troops can't take much more of this. They're really fed up.'

'Have faith, Joshua,' God tells him. 'Go and get them to practise tomorrow's victory shout.'

'Ahem … er … we've got to practise our victory shout,' Joshua tells the soldiers.

'What victory shout?' The soldiers look blank.

'You know – the one we all yell while we're marching round the city for the seventh time tomorrow. I want the advance guard to shout "Glory"*AG and the priests to shout "Hallelujah"*T and the rear guard to shout "Victory"*RG. So let's hear it.'

*'Glory! *Hallelujah! *Victory!' the soldiers mutter.

'Louder!' cries Joshua.

*'Glory! *Hallelujah! *Victory!'

'Again.'

*'Glory! *Hallelujah! *Victory!'

'All right. Off you go,' Joshua sighs. He can only hope they'll sound more convincing tomorrow.

Saturday morning dawns bright and clear. Gloomily Joshua drags himself to his feet and puts on his armour. It weighs a ton. He's never felt less like leading an army. But there's no getting out of it. He grits his teeth and obeys God's commands.

The soldiers obey too. Left… right… left… right… They set off in their usual formation: advance guard, trumpeters, priests with covenant box, rear guard. The going is as tough as ever to begin with as the inhabitants of Jericho jostle for places on the ramparts, booing and yahooing. But there's a change of routine today. Saturday is the seventh day… the day God has told the Israelites to keep marching round and round…

By the time Joshua's men are into their third lap of the city the enemy are beginning to sound rattled. '*Cowardy, cowardy flat feet* – hey, look, they're going round again. *Couldn't fight for goat's meat* – what do you make of that?' Nobody knows quite what to make of it. But everyone senses a threat.

So where's this threat coming from?

The Israelites aren't doing anything very different. They're just marching round with their trumpets and covenant box the way they've done for the past six days. Nothing very threatening in that.

Ah, but you see, suddenly the enemy have realised that the Israelites aren't marching alone. You know that box they're carrying? The covenant box. Well, that box represents God's presence with his people. And it's suddenly dawned on these hecklers and jeerers that God himself is out there circling their city. Of course the Israelites sense God's presence too. His word has dropped from their heads to their hearts, and their spirits are rising with every step. They don't care now what anyone thinks or says. They *know* they aren't a bunch of weaklings parading pointlessly round in circles. They are God's people fighting God's battle God's way.

As the Israelites prepare to march round the city for the seventh and final time, the spectators flee from the ramparts. 'It's no good,' they mutter as they huddle together, trembling. 'The God of Israel is fighting against us.'

Outside the very air seems to crackle with expectancy. Joshua raises his arm. 'Five ... four ... three ... two ... one.'

'Glory! Hallelujah! Victory!' the Israelites yell.*A

And the earth shakes. The thick walls of Jericho crack like eggshells. With a thunderous CRASH, they tumble to the ground.

As promised, God has delivered Jericho, with its king and all its brave soldiers, into the Israelites' hands. But his people have done more than gain a foothold in the land. They've learnt a valuable lesson. Once again they've proved that the greatest victories aren't won by force, but by faith and obedience to God's word.

TELLING THIS STORY TO A GROUP:

With marching feet, trumpets, silence and victory shouts, there's plenty of scope for sound effects here.

As the action develops divide the group into three sections (advance guard, trumpeters and rear guard) and introduce sound effects as indicated * (A= all; AG = advance guard; T= trumpeters; RG= rear guard).

NB: A roll of drums and crash of cymbals (either live or pre-recorded) is an effective way of simulating collapsing walls at the end.

SUGGESTED SONGS:

Be bold, Be strong (JP 14) (CPW 11) (K 17)

I hear the sound of the army of the Lord (JP 100)

I may never march in the infantry (JP 101)

In the name of Jesus (JP 111)

Joshua fit the battle of Jericho (JP 143)

Now be strong and very courageous (JP 172)

Stand up, stand up for Jesus (JP 226)

God told Joshua to take Jericho (JP 351)

We are soldiers of the King (JP 483)

Eighth Time Lucky

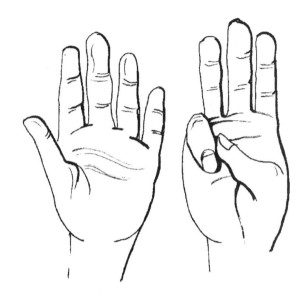

LENGTH: 5–6 minutes

TEACHING POINT: God does not see us as we appear to other people. He knows us as we really are.

BIBLE READING: This story is based on 1 Samuel 16:1–13

For many years the prophet Samuel passed God's word on faithfully to the Israelite people. He settled their arguments and gave them spiritual leadership. But there was a time, not long before he died, when this great man felt sad and depressed. He would lie in bed at night unable to sleep, seeing nothing but failures. Time and time again, it seemed, the people he'd loved and guided had let God down.

First there'd been his own sons Joel and Abijah. Instead of serving God honestly, they'd taken bribes. Then there'd been the whole Israelite nation.

Instead of being content to live under God's rule, they'd demanded an earthly king to rule over them. And finally there was Saul … .

At the thought of Saul tears would spring to the old man's eyes. He well remembered the day when he had anointed him as Israel's first king. The young man had seemed so promising – so eager to keep God's law. But in the years that followed, although he'd been outwardly successful, he'd let God down – not just once but again and again until God had rejected him. Telling Saul he'd lost God's support had been the hardest thing Samuel ever had to do. It wasn't just that he loved Saul and hated to see the mess he'd made of his life. He worried about the future.

'I thought I'd be able to die in peace, knowing the man of God's choosing was on the throne,' he muttered as he tossed and turned through the long night hours. 'That won't happen now.'

And then, one evening, God challenged him.

'How long will you keep grieving over Saul?' God asked. 'I have rejected him. So get some olive oil and go to Bethlehem to the house of a man called Jesse. I've picked one of his sons to be king.'

As usual there was no ignoring that quiet inner voice. Despite his sadness, Samuel knew he had to act.

'Bring a calf with you and say you've come to Bethlehem to offer a sacrifice,' God went on. 'Invite Jesse to take part.'

The city leaders got a bit panicky when they saw Samuel striding in through the city gates.

'The prophet Samuel! Coming here! What does he want?'

It was a big relief to discover he hadn't come to accuse them of some sort of wrongdoing.

'Oh, it's for a sacrifice. Well, what could be nicer!' they beamed. 'We'll get ready for the ceremony straight away.'

Meanwhile in a nearby house Jesse's wife bustled around sorting out eight clean tunics and eight clean cloaks for her husband and sons. 'Did you hear the latest? My boys have been invited to offer a sacrifice with the prophet Samuel,' she told her next-door neighbour proudly.

When everything was organised Samuel and the city leaders gathered round the altar, while Jesse and his seven sons (all dressed in their Sabbath best) trooped towards them up the hill. Samuel's heart skipped a beat as he watched their approach. Just imagine! Somewhere among that group of fine young men was the new king of Israel. The big question was, though: Which young man had God picked?

Tall handsome Eliab was first to make it to the top. 'Hmm. Very impressive,' Samuel thought as he eyed him up and down. And indeed Jesse's eldest son did seem perfect for the job. He had the looks. He had the bearing. But just as the prophet was about to reach for his olive oil, the still small voice whispered, 'No.'

'No?' Samuel queried.

'You're judging by appearances,' God pointed out. 'Just remember. Man goes by what he sees on the outside, but I look at the heart.'

Next in line was Abinadad – another fine specimen of manhood. Again Samuel was about to reach for the olive oil. And again the still small voice said, 'No.'

Next came Shammah. 'Sorry. I haven't picked Shammah either,' said God.

Shammah was followed, in quick succession, by Nethanel, Raddai, Ozem and a final seventh son whose name Samuel didn't quite catch. 'No,' 'No,' 'No,' 'No,' God said to each of them. It was all very disappointing. If Samuel hadn't been such an experienced prophet he might have been tempted to think he'd been brought to Bethlehem on a wild-goose chase. But Samuel knew God better than that. There had to be some other explanation.

'Have you any more sons?' he asked Jesse hopefully.

'Oh, you mean my youngest lad? He's out taking care of the sheep.'

'Send for him,' Samuel ordered. 'We won't offer the sacrifice until he comes.'

A little while later Jesse came puffing back up the hill with his eighth son in tow. 'This is ... David,' he panted.

Strong build, rosy cheeks, two dark eyes sparkling with humour and intelligence. Samuel eyed the lad and instantly liked what he saw. He smiled. He couldn't help it. And then – what a relief! – he heard God's still small voice say, 'That's the one.'

Out, at long last, came the olive oil. Samuel got David to kneel down and poured it on his head. 'Praise God!' The lad lifted his hands to heaven and Samuel's burden of sadness disappeared. It was a happy day for Israel. He could see that in David God had found a ruler who would serve him for the whole of his life with the whole of his heart.

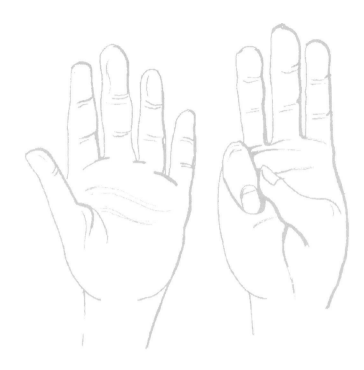

SUGGESTED SONGS:

Give me oil in my lamp, keep me burning (JP 50) (K 66)

He who would valiant be (JP 80) (CPW 82)

Hushed was the evening hymn (JP 85)

I met Jesus at the crossroads (JP 102)

I want to live for Jesus ev'ry day (JP 122)

This little light of mine (JP 258) (K 343)

If you love Me you will obey My commandments (JP 387)

Now Saul was rejected as king of the land (JP 433)

Perfect Timing

LENGTH: 6–7 minutes

TEACHING POINT: Knowing God is in control helps us beat worry.

BIBLE READING: This story is based on 2 Kings 4:8–37
and 2 Kings 8:1–6.

O n the outskirts of Samaria two travellers – a woman and her son – sat in
the shade of a tree sharing a simple meal. The woman's clothes were fine
but shabby, as if she had once been wealthy but had fallen upon hard times.
  'We'll soon be home now, won't we Mum?' the boy said eagerly.
  'We must see the king first.' With a sigh the woman packed up the
remaining scraps of bread. 'When we left Shunem he took control of our
property. We've no guarantee he'll give it back.'

'You mean, he'll hold on to *our* house and fields!' The boy looked shocked. 'But that's not fair. I mean, it wasn't our fault that we had to leave. There was a famine.'

'There was indeed,' his mother agreed. 'What's more, the prophet Elisha said we should go.'

'Did he say what would happen when we came back?'

'No.' Though the woman shook her head wearily her expression was calm. She'd faced many difficulties over the past seven years, living in a foreign land, not having much money. It had been especially hard when her husband died. Still, she was certain it had been the right thing to leave Shunem. And she was equally sure it was now the right thing to return. 'Stop worrying!' She squeezed her son's shoulder. 'God's in control. He'll work things out.'

But beating worry is easier said than done.

'You say God's in control, but how do you *know?*' The boy frowned as they set off along the dusty road.

'From experience. I've seen him do so many wonderful things.'

'Such as?'

'Well, you remember how Elisha used to stay in our home.'

The boy nodded. 'You'd given him his own little room.'

'That's right. And one day, when he was staying with us, he prophesied that your father and I would have a son. It seemed incredible! We'd been married for years without having any children. But sure enough at around the same time the following year you arrived.'

'You mean, God knew about me even before I was born!' The boy's eyes widened.

'You were his surprise gift to us,' the woman went on. 'The most precious gift we'd ever had. And then, one morning, you fell dangerously ill. Within hours your breathing stopped...'

'You mean, I almost *died.*'

'I mean, you *really* died.'

'So how come I'm here?'

'You're here because God has the power of life and death.' The woman paused for a moment and looked up at the surrounding hills. 'I felt sure what had happened couldn't be his will for you – not after the way he'd given you to us. So I carried you up into Elisha's room and laid you on his bed. Without even telling your father the terrible news I rode as fast as I could to Mount

Carmel – that's where Elisha was staying. When I got there, Elisha gave his prophet's stick to his servant Gehazi and sent him on ahead to see if holding it over your body would bring you back to life.'

'And did it?'

'No. When we got to the house Gehazi told us there'd been no change. But Elisha didn't give up. He made me wait outside the bedroom while he went inside to pray. Next thing I heard him calling Gehazi, and then Gehazi called me. I didn't know what I'd find behind that door. But there you were, happy and healthy, sitting on the prophet's knee.'

After hearing that the boy felt quite cheerful. When they finally reached the royal palace, though, his whistling stopped. This talk of the past was all very well. The question was: Could they trust God for the future?

Meanwhile inside the palace King Joram was chatting to Gehazi. The king was keen to find out as much as he could about Elisha's powers. Gehazi had just been talking of one of his master's most unforgettable miracles – the one where he had brought the dead son of a Shunammite woman back to life – when a door at the back of the hall swung open.

'There's a woman here to see the king.' An official ushered our travellers inside.

Nervously they made their way to the throne. The woman began to make her appeal, but King Joram totally ignored her. People were always pestering him – pleading for this, begging for that. At the best of times he only listened with half an ear. And then he noticed the expression on Gehazi's face. The servant was staring in open-mouthed amazement. 'Why, this is the very woman I was telling you about,' he cried. 'And this is the boy Elisha brought back to life.'

'Well I never!' Suddenly the two visitors had the king's complete attention. Here indeed was a turn-up for the books. 'Bring these travellers some refreshment,' he ordered. Then, as the woman sipped her wine and the boy stuffed himself with figs, he took them through Gehazi's story.

'Did Elisha really bring your son here back to life?'

'Oh yes, your majesty, indeed he did,' the woman said eagerly. 'It was like this....'

By the time she'd finished her account of what happened the king had reached two conclusions. One – Elisha's powers were even greater than he'd thought. Two – this woman and her son were the prophet's personal friends so he'd better be careful how he treated them.

'Now what was it you wanted to see me about?' he inquired.

'About our property in Shunem,' the woman ventured. 'You took it over and we'd like it back.'

'A simple matter!' The king turned to the official. 'Make sure this good lady gets back everything she owns. And while you're at it, see she's paid for all the crops her fields have produced over the last seven years.'

The official gasped. He'd never known the king to be so generous. He was still in a state of shock when the delighted travellers took their leave. 'If you ask me, your master's God had a hand in that,' he told Gehazi.

'My thoughts exactly,' Gehazi smiled.

SUGGESTED SONGS:

Ask! Ask! Ask! and it shall be given you (JP 11)

Be bold, Be strong (JP 14) (CPW 11) (K 17)

Be still and know that I am God (JP 22)

God is our guide, our light and our deliverer (JP 56)

I'm very glad of God (JP 107)

My God is so big (JP 169) (CPW 157) (K 255)

Surely goodness and mercy shall follow me (JP 223)

Did you ever talk to God above? (JP 329)

Jehovah Jireh, God will provide (JP 404) (CPW 121) (K 190)

Lord, You are brilliant, champion of champions (JP 423)

The Boat Trip

LENGTH: Basic story 5–6 minutes. (You will need to allow extra time for sound effects.)

TEACHING POINT: At first the disciples did not realise who Jesus was. Jesus still waits for people to realise who he is today.

BIBLE READING: This story is based on Mark 4:35–41.

Picture a big freshwater lake so long you can't see from one end to the other, so wide it takes several hours to sail across, and so deep two elephants, two rhinoceroses and a giraffe could stand on the sandy bottom one on top of the other, and the giraffe's neck still wouldn't break the surface of the water. This lake is full of fish. (It's a good thing we only imagined the wild animals otherwise the fish might die of shock!) Usually a gentle breeze plays upon its surface.* And the waves lap softly against the shore.* But every now and again a sudden wind sweeps down from the hills,* whipping the waves up into a fury.* For a few hours the storm will rage.* And then everything gets back to normal.

The lake is called the Sea of Galilee and it's famous because a great deal of Jesus' teaching and preaching took place on its shores. His base – Capernaum – was a lakeside town. And a number of his disciples were local fishermen. So let's imagine Jesus into the picture. Let's picture him standing in a boat a few metres from the shore teaching the huge crowd who have gathered to hear him. It's late afternoon and he's been talking to them for hours, telling them lots of different parables. (Parables are stories with a spiritual meaning.) As usual, even though many of the listeners aren't sure what these parables mean, no one is in any hurry to go home. They're out for the day – which is nice for them, but hard on the speaker. By this stage Jesus is worn out.

So here's what he decides to do. He gets the disciples to push the boat out a bit further from the shore. Then he tells them to climb back on board, hoist the sail, and away they go, heading for the opposite side of the lake.

'Whew! I'm not sorry to see the back of that lot.' Peter heaves a sigh of relief as the crowd disappears from view.

'Yeah. There must have been thousands of them,' his companions agree.

They're feeling rather smug. It's great being able to sail away with Jesus. They're looking forward to their own private teaching session when he'll tell them exactly what his parables mean.

'You know, sometimes I wonder why the Master takes so much out of himself talking to crowds. Most people haven't a clue what he's on about,' says Peter.

Andrew nods. 'When he told them today that the kingdom of heaven was like a mustard seed, they probably thought they'd get closer to God by planting one in their gardens.'

'When really he meant his kingdom might have small beginnings but it will grow really big,' finishes Matthew.

Then they all look round to see if Jesus is impressed by their cleverness.

But Jesus, exhausted by all his teaching and preaching, has fallen asleep on a cushion at the back of the boat.

'Shhh. Keep your voices down,' Peter warns. 'We don't want to wake him.'

Meanwhile the stiff* little breeze has become stronger.*
And the waves lapping round the side of the boat have become higher.*
And the sky overhead has grown darker.
'I don't like this! I feel sick,' says Thomas.
Some of the other disciples don't like it either, but the fishermen among them are glad of the chance to show off their skills. As the lake begins to heave and thrash they lower the sails and grab the oars.
'Hang onto the sides. We're in for a rough ride,' predicts Peter.
With that the little boat is caught up in the most terrible storm. The wind howls down from the hills.* The waves explode all around them.* One minute the boat is lurching sideways up a mountain of water, next thing it's plunging down the other side. Peter's made some risky crossings in his time – but this is *the worst*. The boat is being hurled around like a piece of driftwood. It could go under at any moment…
'Well, what are you waiting for? *Wake Jesus!*' Peter yells.
'Wake up, Master,' the disciples cry. 'Don't you care that we're *drowning?*'
Poor Jesus! He never gets a minute's peace. If it's not one thing it's another. Here he is being woken out of a sound sleep by a crowd of panicking disciples. So what's all this about then? He pulls himself to his feet. For a moment he takes in the crashing, thrashing, shrieking, squalling duet of wind and waves.* Then he raises his hand. 'Quiet! Be still!' he orders.
And immediately the wind shuts up.*
And the waves smooth out.*
And everything is calm.
Wow! The disciples don't quite know what they expected, but it certainly wasn't this. In some ways Jesus calming the storm is more scary than the storm itself. At least storms are natural. But a human being telling the wind and waves what to do – that's *awesome!*
They hardly dare look Jesus in the face.
'What's wrong now? Why are you so afraid? Have you still no faith?' he inquires gently.
They know he's asking them to believe something. When they left the shore they thought they were sailing away with an expert religious teacher who made them feel superior to the rest of the world. But now – after *that* performance – they don't know what to think. So they scratch their heads, struggling to come to terms with what's happened. Who *is* this man, they ask

themselves. What sort of a person can command the wind and waves?

Jesus doesn't seize the opportunity to make any dramatic claims for himself. He's not the sort of God who forces belief down anyone's throat. He's there. And he loves them. And he's prepared to be patient.

So he just sits back and enjoys the rest of the trip.

TELLING THIS STORY TO A GROUP:

Involve your listeners by dividing them into 'wind' and 'waves'. Use cue cards to indicate the different levels of sound effects required, ie, SOFT; MEDIUM; LOUD; SOFT BUT FIERCE. Rehearse effects using these cards. Then tell the story bringing in appropriate levels of wind and waves as indicated.* (NB: SOFT BUT FIERCE should create the effect of an ongoing storm without drowning out the voice of the storyteller!)

SUGGESTED SONGS:

By blue Galilee Jesus walked of old (JP 23)

Come let us sing of a wonderful love (JP 29)

Come to Jesus, 'He's amazing' (JP 33)

Do you want a Pilot? (JP 40)

Go, tell it on the mountain (JP 65) (CPW 54)

Put your hand in the hand of the man who stilled the water (JP 206)

Who took fish and bread, hungry people fed? (JP 286)

With Jesus in the boat we can smile at the storm (JP 291)

It was Jesus who taught His disciples (JP 397)

True Greatness

LENGTH: Basic story 6 minutes. (You will need to allow extra time for groups to learn and repeat their catch-phrases.)

TEACHING POINT: True greatness – the difference between what the world believes and what Jesus teaches.

BIBLE READING: Mark 10:33–37

Jesus and his disciples were walking back to their base in Capernaum. It had been a long, busy day and they were hot, tired and hungry. Out in front strode Peter – big and broad. A real action man was Peter – the sort whose mouth and feet kept sprinting on ahead of his brain.* By his side – struggling a little to keep up – was Andrew. Andrew and Peter were brothers. And if Peter was the bigger and stronger of the two, Andrew liked to think he was the more experienced.

He'd spent some time with John the Baptist – something Peter had never done. And it was he, Andrew, who had first brought his brother to Jesus. *

Close behind Peter and Andrew came another set of brothers, laughing and joking at the top of their voices. Things were never quiet when James and John were around. 'Sons of Thunder', Jesus called them. The nickname may have sprung from their childhood days, for it is thought that they were Jesus' cousins.*

Matthew, Philip and Thomas came next, closely followed by another James, while Simon, Thaddeus, Bartholomew and Judas brought up the rear.

Left … right … left … right. … The twelve men trudged along the dusty road. They weren't saying much now. Even James and John had fallen silent … until suddenly Peter came up with a question.

'What do you think it will be like when our Master becomes King?' he asked.

'Brilliant!' said Thomas.

'No hoofing it then,' cried Andrew. 'We'll ride around in chariots.'

'There'll be a banquet every night,' said Philip, licking his lips.

'That's right.' Peter looked dreamy. 'I can just see us sitting round the table, with me up there beside King Jesus at the top.'

'Hey! What makes you think you'll be the one sitting beside him?' demanded Matthew.

There was a sudden hush.

'Well, it's obvious, isn't it? I'm the leader,' said Peter.

'Oh no you're not.'

'Oh yes I am. I'm always first at everything.'

'You certainly weren't the first to meet Jesus,' said Andrew. 'I was the one who introduced you, so I deserve the place of honour at his table.'

'Hold on a minute.' Now James burst into the conversation. 'If we're talking about places of honour, well, it stands to reason my brother and I should sit next to Jesus. I mean, we're family. We've known him all our lives.'

'The top places in the kingdom of heaven are ours,' agreed John.

'Oh no they aren't!'

'Oh yes they are!'

The argument went on all the way to Capernaum.*

'What were you lot quarrelling about on the road?' Jesus asked when they got back to base.

Oh dear! They'd thought he'd been walking far enough ahead not to notice the noise.

'Nothing. Nothing at all!' said Peter airily.

His companions hung their heads and looked embarrassed.

To their relief Jesus let the matter drop. 'Come and sit down. We'll have a little talk before supper.' He beckoned them over to the mat.

Now when you're feeling hungry and someone wants to have a talk, well it can be a bit hard to concentrate, can't it? But the minute the disciples heard what Jesus wanted to talk about, he had their complete attention.

'I want to tell you how to be great in God's kingdom,' he said.

Amazing! Their quarrel was about to be settled once and for all.

'Whoever wants to be first,' Jesus began...

'Go on! Tell them whoever wants to be first must be a born leader,' thought Peter.

'Go on! Tell them whoever wants to be first should get himself related to a king,' thought John.

'Go on! Tell them whoever wants to be first must have lots of experience,' thought Andrew.

'Whoever wants to be first,' said Jesus, 'must place himself last of all and be the servant of all.'

The disciples' jaws dropped. Surely if you wanted to be first you had to beat the opposition. You had to prove you were cleverer, richer, better-looking and more powerful than everyone else. And then, as the Master's words sank in, it all began to make sense. Peter and Andrew looked sheepish. James and John shrugged wryly. We might have guessed, those looks said. All along Jesus had been teaching them that his kingdom was different from any other kingdom they'd ever known. So it stood to reason the path to greatness in his kingdom would be different too.

'We've got to stop trying to beat people and aim to help them instead. Right?' said Peter.

Jesus didn't answer him directly. Instead he called over a small child: a child from a local family – with no obvious gifts – who'd done very little in life. He got this child to stand close beside him and then he gave the child a big hug.

And the disciples smiled. How silly their arguments seemed now! It was all so simple really. What counted in God's kingdom wasn't how clever you were or how much you'd done. What counted was keeping close to Jesus, being loved by him, and loving him back

TELLING THIS STORY TO A GROUP:

Involve children by splitting the group into three: Peters, Andrews, and James and Johns. Each group has a rhythmic catch-phrase. Peter's catch-phrase is 'I'm a born leader.' Andrew's is 'Without me, where would you be?' James' and John's is 'Family first.' As the different characters are introduced, the groups repeat their catch-phrase. When the argument breaks out they all shout their catch-phrases at the same time. (The appropriate points are marked with an asterisk in the text.) The youngest child in the group should be seated beside the story-teller, being brought forward at the end to represent the child Jesus used as an illustration. (NB: only do this if you are sure it will not cause embarrassment. Ideally the child should be a pre-schooler.)

SUGGESTED SONGS:

Big man standing by the blue waterside (JP 16) (K 422)

I'm special because God has loved me (JP 106) (CPW 115) (K 162)

Jesus' hands were kind hands, doing good to all (JP 134) (CPW 124) (K 194)

Make me a servant, humble and meek (JP 162)

We have a king who rides a donkey (JP 264)

Whether you're one or whether you're two (JP 284) (K 384)

I want to tell you (I want to tell you) (JP 375)

If you want to be great in God's kingdom (JP 389)

Account Number 54321

LENGTH: 5 minutes

TEACHING POINT: Jesus used this parable to show that we can't expect God to forgive us if we aren't prepared to forgive others.

BIBLE READING: The story is based on Matthew 18:21–35

Picture a servant waiting outside the throne room, shaking in his sandals. He's been foolish. For the last few years he's spent a lot more than he's earned and now he owes the king thousands of pounds. Any minute now the door of the throne room will open and he'll be expected to repay the money. Except he can't repay the money. He hasn't any property. Or savings. What he does have is a wife and children. And they're the ones who'll suffer for his stupidity.

So he sits there feeling like a criminal about to cross the Niagara Falls on a tightrope in a force nine gale. 'I've made such a mess of things,' he groans. 'I've been so foolish. If only I could have another chance…'

Suddenly the door opens. Armed guards escort the miserable servant into the room. Left … right … left … right. A dozen paces and he stands before the king.

'Account number 54321,' the guards announce.

'54321.' The king consults a scroll, then looks up, frowning. 'You're in the red,' he says sternly. 'In fact you're so badly in the red you're practically crimson. What do you have to say for yourself?'

The servant hangs his head. 'Nothing,' he mutters.

'And are you here to pay off this debt?'

'Please … if I could just have a few more years … I mean … months.'

'I want to settle my accounts *now*, not some time towards the end of the next millennium,' pronounces the king. 'There's only one thing for it. I shall have to sell you and your wife and children as slaves.'

Slaves! The servant turns white. He falls to his knees.

'Be patient with me, your majesty,' he implores, 'and I will pay you everything!'

Fat chance! The guards roll their eyes and close in on the servant, ready for the command to take him away.

But the king is looking thoughtful.

He places a hand on the servant's shoulder. 'You've got yourself into a real mess,' he says. 'You won't be able to pay that money back. Not today. Not tomorrow. Not in a million years.'

'You're right,' the servant gulps, pinning his hopes on the compassionate crinkle he sees round his master's eyes.

'Very well.' With a scratch of the stylus the king draws a line through account number 54321. 'I've cancelled your debt.'

'You mean … that's it … I can go…?'

The king nods. The guards shrug. And the servant almost somersaults out of the throne room.

Next thing he's striding jauntily down the street, swinging his arms and humming under his breath. No more debt! Wonderful! Perhaps he'll take himself off to the nearest inn and celebrate over dinner. Then it hits him. He can't afford dinner. He may not have any debts, but he has no cash either. And no sensible innkeeper will let him eat now and pay later.

But here's a stroke of luck. He's just caught sight of Genius on the other side of the street.

'Oi, Genius. Over here!' he yells.

Genius is one of our servant's fellow servants. Genius isn't his real name, of course. It's a nickname. The truth is Genius isn't very bright. Not being very bright means he isn't much good with money. Instead of making his wages last the full week, Genius spends all he's earned in the first few days, which means that by the middle of the week he's flat broke.

And our servant has just remembered something. Once, when Genius was broke, he'd lent him the price of a meal.

Now he grabs his fellow servant by the throat.

'Pay back what you owe me,' he hisses between clenched teeth.

There's a moment of desperate fumbling as Genius pulls his money-bag out from under his cloak.

Good! He's got the message. Our servant stands back, folds his arms, and waits.

But what's this? Genius is peering anxiously into his money-bag. He's shaking it. He's turning it inside out and shaking it again just to make absolutely sure. 'S-s-sorry!' Genius throws himself to his knees. 'You know I never have any money on third days. But I'll pay you back. Honest, I will. Just give me until the end of the week.'

'What a fool!' our servant thinks as he watches poor old Genius grovelling in the dust. 'There's no way I'm giving *him* a second chance.'

So, after this brief period of reflection, he turns round and has Genius thrown into jail.

End of story?

No, not quite.

Some of the other servants are pretty upset when they hear what has happened to Genius and they mention the matter to the king.

Before long our servant finds himself back in the throne room. And this time the king is anything but sympathetic.

'You reptile!' he thunders. 'I forgave you everything you owed me, just because you asked me to. Why didn't you have mercy on your fellow servant the way I had mercy on you?'

Well, there's no answer to that, is there? Our servant has behaved abominably. The king reaches for his scroll and his stylus and undeletes debt number 54321.

'Throw the wretch into jail and keep him there,' he orders, 'until the last penny has been paid.'

TELLING THIS STORY TO A GROUP:

The story has plenty of action and should work well as a mime for five characters: the king, the servant, two guards and Genius.

SUGGESTED SONGS:

God forgave my sin in Jesus' name (JP 54)

He paid a debt He did not owe (JP 77)

Make me a channel of Your peace (JP 161) (K 248)

Our Father who is in heaven (JP 192) (CPW 171)

Put your hand in the hand of the man who stilled the water (JP 206)

God of all mercy (JP 350)

Sometimes I'm naughty (JP 460)

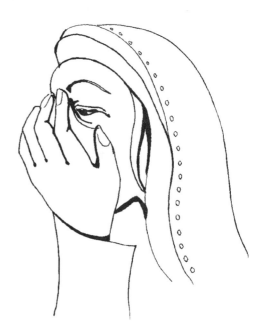

Meet Mary

LENGTH: 6 minutes

TEACHING POINT: Jesus conquered sin and death. He died and rose again.

BIBLE READING: This story is based on Luke 8:1–3; John 19:25; Luke 23:55–56; 24:1–7; John 20:11–18.

Hello. My name is Mary, and I'm here today to tell you my story. But first I'll let you into a secret. When I got the invitation to come and meet you I nearly said no. 'They'll be bored,' I told myself. 'Anyone who has read the New Testament already knows all about me.' And then I remembered just how many different Marys there are in the New Testament and how easy it is to get those Marys mixed up and I decided to come after all.

So here I am – ready to help you settle your Mary questions. I'm not Mary the mother of Jesus. And I'm not Mary the mother of James and John. Nor am I the

Mary Jesus used to call on in Bethany – the one with the sister called Martha and the brother Lazarus. I'm Mary Magdalene – the Mary Jesus healed.

You'll have gathered that up until the time I met Jesus I wasn't very well. In fact I was pretty sick. What's worse – it wasn't a straightforward physical problem. I wasn't blind or deaf or paralysed like some of the other folk Jesus healed. My sickness was spiritual, and it was so bad I hardly knew who I was or what I was doing. 'Steer clear of that Mary Magdalene. She's possessed by demons.' That's what people said.

And then along came Jesus – the first person I'd ever met who understood my crazy behaviour. 'Help me – please help me.' I threw myself at his feet. And he just laid his hands on me – such tender loving hands – and ordered the demons to go. People said afterwards that in a matter of seconds my whole appearance changed. All I know is that I felt free for the first time in years.

So what was I going to do with my new-found freedom? Well, the answer seemed pretty obvious. I owed it to Jesus, so I decided to follow him. Now here's a funny thing. Almost everyone you talk to can reel off the names of at least four male disciples. Everyone knows Jesus worked with twelve men. But ask them about the women and their faces go blank. Yet there was a band of women with Jesus, supporting him and his team out of their own pockets. There was me, my friend Joanna, and another friend, Susanna. Then there was Mary, the mother of James and John, and a few more besides. Like the Twelve, we believed Jesus was more than a brilliant teacher. Like them, we were looking forward to the time when he would become King.

And then – in a matter of days – our whole world fell apart. I expect you already know why. You don't need me to tell you what happened to Jesus. Looking back, I suppose we should have seen it coming. I mean, we all knew he had fallen foul of the religious authorities. We knew they wanted to kill him. We just never thought they'd succeed.

The day of the crucifixion was the worst day of my life. I was there with Mary, his mother and Mary, the mother of James and John. We saw it all – the nails, the crown of thorns. For six agonising hours we watched Jesus hang on the cross. We saw the sky darken. We heard him cry out to God. We saw his head slump forward in death.

Devastated – that would be the word to describe us. But at least afterwards there was something I could do. Once the soldier stuck his spear into Jesus' side, and I knew he really was dead, I met up with the other women and we went to prepare spices to rub on his body. Of course we couldn't take them to the grave immediately because the next day was the Sabbath. So we arranged to go on Sunday morning first thing.

It was the thought of seeing Jesus one last time that kept me going over the next twenty-four hours. I kept telling myself his death had been a triumph. The religious authorities might have killed him. But his goodness and spiritual authority had shone through right to the end.

Then Joanna dropped in on her way from the synagogue. 'We've a problem,' she told me. 'The Pharisees said Jesus' disciples might try to steal his body. So Pilate's had the tomb guarded. There's a huge stone blocking the door.'

If it had meant flattening the guards and hiring a team of horses to shift that boulder, I wasn't going to let any scheming Pharisee stand in our way. 'Don't worry! We'll get in,' I vowed.

And of course we did. Effortlessly. When we arrived at the tomb next morning the stone had been rolled away and there wasn't a guard to be seen. That was the first surprise. The second surprise was that Jesus' body wasn't to be seen either. It had disappeared.

For the next half-hour I was in a state of shock. Even though two men in gleaming robes appeared and told us Jesus had risen, I couldn't take it in. One minute I was hoping the gleaming men might be right and that he really was alive. The next I was sure the body had been stolen.

I ended up in floods of tears, hanging about outside the tomb after everyone else had gone. And by everyone I don't just mean the other women–Peter and John had been there too.

And then it happened.

My sight was so blurred I didn't recognise him to begin with. I thought he was the gardener and just babbled on about Jesus' body being stolen and not knowing where to look.

'Mary,' he said.

And the moment I heard that voice, I knew.

Jesus was with me in the garden. Totally alive. But alive in a totally new way. With a sort of forever-aliveness. An aliveness only someone who has beaten death can have.

So there you are. That's my story. And if you're ever asked what was the first word Jesus spoke on Easter Sunday morning, I hope you'll remember it was my name. I also hope you'll remember which of the New Testament Marys I am. But don't worry if you forget. Who I am and what happened to me isn't so important. It's what Jesus did that counts.

He rose from the dead.

What's more, he shares his special forever-aliveness with everyone who trusts him – so you and I can beat death too!

TELLING THIS STORY TO A GROUP:

The story is a dramatic monologue. Ideally it requires two people: one to introduce the special visitor (giving a few clues to her identity) and to thank her afterwards; the second (in costume) to play the part of Mary.

SUGGESTED SONGS:

Alleluia, alleluia, give thanks to the risen Lord! (JP 3)

God's not dead (No) (JP 60) (CPW 66) (K 85)

He is Lord (JP 75)

Jesus Christ is risen today, Hallelujah! (JP 130)

Led like a lamb (JP 151)

Low in the grave He lay (JP 159)

One day when heaven was filled with His praises (JP 187)

Saviour of the world, thank You for dying on the cross (JP 216)

This joyful Eastertide (JP 256)

Yours be the glory! risen, conquering Son (JP 299)

It's easy to be a believer (JP 400)

The Lord is risen today! (JP 469)

The Promise

LENGTH: 5 minutes

TEACHING POINT: The Holy Spirit gives us the power to witness effectively for Christ.

BIBLE READING: This story is based on Acts 1:1–14 and Acts 2:1–41.

Jesus' followers have spent the last few days in Jerusalem, gathered together in an upper room. Jesus himself has just gone back to heaven, but before leaving he's told them what he wants them to do. They are to be his witnesses: first in Jerusalem ('That's OK,' they think. 'We're here already'); then in Judea and Samaria (Hmm – that's going to mean a bit of travel) and finally to the ends of the earth (Pardon, Jesus? Come again?). Yes, it's stunning. But that's what Jesus said: Jerusalem, Judea and Samaria, and *the ends of the earth.*

'In other words, we've got the job of telling the *whole world* about Jesus,' says Peter afterwards.

Thomas looks decidedly apprehensive. 'OK, so that's plan A. I vote for plan B.'

But there is no plan B.

Still Thomas isn't alone in his fears and apprehensions. Now that Jesus has gone back to his Father, the believers – men and women – are all wondering what the future holds. He's given them a job, but from where they're sitting it looks incredibly difficult, and incredibly dangerous; the Jews have just put Jesus to death after all. The chances are they'll want to get rid of his followers too.

'You're not suggesting we chicken out, are you?' James asks at one point.

All round the room heads shake firmly. Nobody has any intention of chickening out of their God-given mission. It's just hard not knowing when, where and how they're meant to begin.

You see, Jesus has told them to wait. 'Don't leave Jerusalem, but wait for the gift my Father has promised,' he's said. 'John baptised with water, but in a few days you will be baptised with the Holy Spirit.'

So that's what they've been doing. Waiting. Not laying plans. Not discussing strategies. Not compiling a training manual: *How to win the world for Christ.* Just waiting. Prayerfully. Before God.

Waiting is never easy. Over the last few days action man Peter has struggled with the feeling that it's a terrible waste of time. Doubting Thomas has struggled not to let the uncertainty rob him of his hard-won faith. Everyone has wondered how long this waiting period will last – one day … two days … a week. No, the waiting has been as hard as climbing a mountain. But somehow this morning it's as if they're finally within reach of the peak.

Meanwhile the outside world is waking up. Today is the Feast of Pentecost – a religious festival celebrating the beginning of the wheat harvest. God-fearing Jews from far and wide have made their way to Jerusalem.

Morning sunlight peeps in through the windows of that upstairs room. And, suddenly, it happens. Whoosh – a sound like a violent wind sweeps through the house. Next thing tongues of fire are flickering above the heads of the praying believers and the Holy Spirit is filling them with power. He takes control of their tongues so that when they burst into joyful worship they're praising God in languages they've never learnt to speak.

The unearthly sound brings passers-by to a standstill. Before long a crowd has gathered outside the house. 'Hey, what's going on up there?' they shout.

'Is it a private party, or can anyone join in?'

Now if the folk in that upstairs room had been in it for the kicks, they would have ignored those outsiders and just kept right on enjoying their mind-boggling, mega-brilliant, super-fantastic spiritual trip. But of course they know that isn't why the Holy Spirit has been given. The new-born church is a church with a mission. So before you can say 'Stuff the Pharisees' out come the members, tumbling down into the street to tell anyone and everyone how wonderful God is.

More and more onlookers gather – folk from dozens of different countries, all asking the same questions: 'What's happened?' 'What's got into these people?' The amazing thing is they all hear the believers talking in their native tongues – which only adds to their curiosity and confusion. It doesn't make sense. Galilean fishermen shouldn't be expert linguists.

In the end Peter takes centre stage. 'Fellow Jews and all you who live in Jerusalem, let me explain this to you.' He goes on to say that what they are seeing is the fulfilment of a prophecy they've read in the Book of Joel, the one where God promised to pour out his Spirit on ordinary people, young and old. And then he points them to Jesus, the source of the gift. 'Repent and be baptised every one of you,' he finishes. 'In the name of Jesus and for the forgiveness of your sins.'

And 3,000 people respond. Yes, around 3,000 people turn away from their old lives and get baptised that very afternoon.

Later – much later – Peter's about to tumble into bed when he notices Thomas sitting there, praising God, with a blissful smile on his face. He knows his fellow disciple well enough to risk a little teasing.

'So how do you feel about plan A now, Tommy?' he winks. 'Remember, the one you didn't vote for...'

'That was *then*,' declares Thomas. 'This is *now* ... and, well, it's obvious, isn't it? Ends of the earth, here we come!'

SUGGESTED SONGS:

All over the world the Spirit is moving (JP 5) (CPW 5)

Brothers and sisters (JP 21)

Colours of day dawn into the mind (JP 28) (CPW 24) (K 433)

For I'm building a people of power (JP 47) (CPW 48) (K 61)

God whose Son was once a man on earth (JP 62)

How lovely on the mountains (JP 84)

Hang on, stand still (JP 356) (CPW 77) (K 94)

I am the Church! You are the Church (JP 367)

Jesus, send me the helper (JP 409) (K 213)

Spirit of God, please fill me now to overflowing (JP 465)

The Spirit lives to set us free (JP 472) (K 334)

What an Answer!

LENGTH: Basic story 5 minutes. You will need to allow extra time for the group to think up their prayer responses.

TEACHING POINT: The Bible shows us the value and importance of praying for others.

BIBLE READING: Acts 12:1–17

Imagine you're a Christian living in Jerusalem around 46 AD. You've come to the home of a woman called Mary to meet with your fellow believers. Usually these meetings are times of celebration. The room is full of smiles and laughter. But today everyone looks worried. There's been a wave of persecution. King Herod, the governor of Palestine, has just executed one of your leaders – the apostle James. And now he's arrested Peter.

Mary comes over to greet you. 'What's the news?' you ask anxiously.

She sighs. 'Not good, I'm afraid. Peter stands trial tomorrow.'

You know what that means. If the Jews have their way, Peter will be put to death. Losing James has been bad. To lose Peter, with all his energy and experience and gifts and vision and powers of leadership ... well, it just doesn't bear thinking about.

But what can you do? A few possibilities flash through your mind. Plead with Herod? (Won't work – Herod has no time for Christians.) Help Peter escape? (No chance – he's chained between two guards.) Run away in case Herod comes after you next? (Tempting – but you're determined not to let God down.) No, there's only one thing for it. You believe in a God who hears and answers prayer. So all you can do is get down on your knees with the rest of the group in that upstairs room and pray your heart out.

*'Help Peter, Lord.' 'Lord, save him.' 'Be with him, Lord,' you pray.

A short distance away, in a cold, smelly dungeon on the outskirts of the city, Peter is praying too – for his wife, for James's brother John, for all his fellow believers. He's got chains round his wrists and a snoring soldier on either side. He knows that this could be his last night on earth. And he certainly doesn't expect to fall asleep. But suddenly he's dreaming – dreaming that the dark cell is full of light and that an angel is shaking him by the shoulder.

'Hurry! Get up!' the angel says. Immediately, with a clink and a clatter, Peter's chains fall to the ground.

'Put on your belt, sandals and cloak and follow me,' the angel tells him.

Next thing they're outside the cell approaching the first guard-post. Will the guard see them? Peter holds his breath. Whew! They've walked past and the soldier hasn't moved a muscle. Second guard-post coming up. Again Peter holds his breath. And exactly the same thing happens. It's as if the soldiers have been paralysed. Peter and the angel keep walking until they reach a heavy iron gate – the final obstacle to freedom. Hey presto! It opens before them like the electronic doors of some twentieth-century supermarket. They march out into the street. And the angel vanishes.

Peter tries to wake himself up. He pinches himself. But nothing changes. He's still outside under the starry sky. Hey, wait a minute! The angel ... the broken chains ... the automatic gate – they really happened. He's free!

'Just wait till everyone hears about this.' He punches the air – and off he goes.

Maybe you can guess where he's heading?

To Mary's house where your prayer meeting is still in full swing.

*'Help Peter, Lord.' 'Lord, save him.' 'Be with him, Lord.'

You're all praying so hard the knock on the door comes as an unwelcome interruption.

'Oh dear! Answer that, would you?' Mary tells Rhoda, her servant.

Rhoda leaves the room and you keep right on praying.

*'Help Peter, Lord.' 'Lord, save him.' 'Be with him, Lord.'

But within a few seconds Rhoda's back – bursting with excitement.

'It's Peter!' she cries.

'What?'

'He's outside the door!'

Poor girl, you think. She's hallucinating!

'Peter can't be outside the door. He's in prison,' Mary points out.

But Rhoda sticks to her story. 'I heard him outside the door. "It's me. Peter. Let me in," he said.'

You all look at each other. The girl couldn't be telling the truth, could she?

'It's me. Peter. Let me in,' a man is yelling down below.

'Funny! That sounds like Peter,' someone says.

'It must be his guardian angel,' someone else says in a very spiritual tone.

A pretty impatient angel, you think to yourself.

Mary leaves the room. You hear her feet on the stairs. There's a creak and a rattle of bolts as she opens the door.

'Peter!' she shouts.

'What did I tell you?' says Rhoda.

'He's here! He's safe.' You rush down the stairs with the rest of the gang and throw yourself at him. Lucky he's such a big man, otherwise he might have escaped Herod's sword only to be hugged to death.

Eventually the hubbub dies down. Peter wants to say something. Shaking his head as if even he still can't quite take in what has happened, he tells you the whole story – from the minute the angel appeared in his cell to the minute he found himself walking down the street.

You listen, scarcely able to believe your ears, thinking back over your part in the rescue.

There you'd been, down on your knees: *'Help Peter, Lord!' 'Lord, save him.' 'Be with him, Lord,' you'd prayed.

You look up at big beaming Peter standing in front of you, large as life.
What a man!
What a God!
What an answer!

TELLING THIS STORY TO A GROUP:

At the first asterisk pause and get the group to think of their own short prayers for Peter. Copy these out on a large sheet of paper. The group then participate in the story by repeating these phrases where indicated throughout the narrative. (This simulated prayer activity is designed to help youngsters grasp the efficacy of prayer. It may be used as a springboard into the real thing – encouraging them to pray for others.)

SUGGESTED SONGS:

Ask! Ask! Ask! and it shall be given you (JP 11)
Daniel was a man of prayer (JP 36)
What a friend we have in Jesus (JP 273) (CPW 228)
Did you ever talk to God above? (JP 329)
His ways are not our ways (JP 364)
Prayer is like a telephone (JP 448) (CPW 176) (K 286)

SONGS PRAYING FOR THE BEREAVED:

Father be with her/his/their family (JP 335)
Father, for our friends we pray (JP 336) (CPW 176)

SUBJECT INDEX A–Z

SCRIPTURE INDEX

50 Bible Dramas For Children

by Lynda Neilands

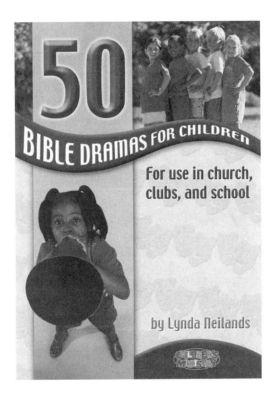

ISBN – 1 84291 253 4

These tried and tested dramas will help today's youngsters engage with the Bible. Not every drama is designed to be performed by children. Some will work better when adults perform them and others are written for a mixture of adult and child performers. At the start of each drama there is an indication of who should ideally perform the script. Each drama also has an application section with explore, chat and think ideas.

100 Instant Children's Talks
by Sue Relf

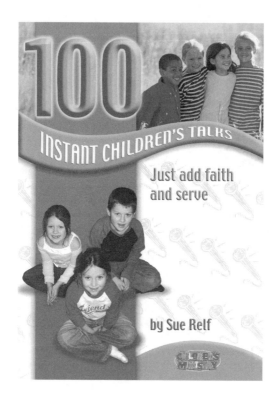

ISBN – 1 84291 290 9

Children's talks are needed to fit many situations – church services, family services, school assemblies, Bible clubs, holiday clubs and missions, regular children's activities and so on. Here are 100 ideas that can be fitted into all of these. The talks are not intended to be slavishly followed; they can be adapted, embellished, shortened, developed or altered in whatever way is necessary in order to make them suitable for the age and background of the children and the situation in which the talk is to be given.

100 Worship Activities
For Children

by Chris Leach

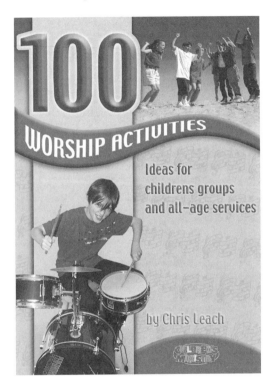

ISBN – 1 84291 297 1

This practical resource gives ideas for activities and games that illustrate the true meaning of worship, to help lead children into a deeper relationship with God. Many are also suitable for all-age services, designed to bring new life and exuberance to your church's worship time. The ideas are listed under seasons of the church year, with full theme and Scripture indexes.

100 Children's Club Activities
by Jan Dyer

ISBN – 1 84291 289 5

More and more churches are discovering the importance of weekday or weekend children's clubs as a way to reach the families in their own local communities. This comprehensive volume features 100 creative activities for children of all ages and from a wide variety of cultural backgrounds, plus detailed guidelines on how to run a children's club, obtain the resources you need and make it a rewarding experience for all involved.